INDOOR AIR

RISKS AND REMEDIES

RICHARD L. CROWTHER, FAIA

**This book was written within the context of prevailing
information. Each person is unique, living within a
complex environment that can have benefits or cause
biologic harm. No endorsement is given as to benefit or
harm that might individually apply from concepts,
sources, resources, or as otherwise stated herein.**

ACKNOWLEDGEMENTS

The author gratefully extends his appreciation for the interest and time expended by the following persons:

Of particular note have been "papers," discussions, and sectional reviews by Dr. Edward Martell, a research scientist at the National Center for Atmospheric Research and by Dr. John Zimmerman of the Bioelectromagnetic Institute; for final review of the manuscript by Ren Anderson of the Solar Energy Research Institute and Don Frey, P.E., of Architectural Energy Corporation; and "papers" of reference by Dr. Gerald Rappe, engaged in electrophoresis effect research.

Appreciation is especially extended to Robert Steimle for his valuable assistance and diligence within the formative structuring of this book and actualization of the desktop publishing.

PREFACE

*The source of oxygenated, life-sustaining **indoor air** is global **outdoor air**.* The oxygen in our global atmosphere originates from the phytoplankton of the seas and from tropical and other forests and vegetation of our planet, through photosynthesis driven by the sun.

Our technologic societies, with a primary dependence on fossil fuels, toxic chemistry, and nuclear and other radioactive processes, are polluting and destroying the life-giving and life-sustaining *vitality* of global air. The future of natural ecosystems, of which we are a dependent part, is in jeopardy. We increase the likelihood of an *extinction of Life on Earth*.

Time is critical to our preservation of and alignment with Nature's regenerative and sustaining ecologic, ecosystemic, and atmospheric vitality. Our survival and future well-being lie within local and international efforts and cooperation to *sustain Life on Earth*.

TABLE OF CONTENTS

PART ONE - OVERVIEW

Introduction 1
The Indoor Problem 3
Our Techno-Society 6
Sensitivities 9
Breathing 12
Oxygen 15

PART TWO - BIOLOGIC EFFECTS

Biologic Stress 21
Biologic Resistance 24
Biosystems 28
"Sick Building Syndrome" 31

PART THREE - OUR ENVIRONS

Built Environment 39
Location and Air Quality 42
Ecologic Architecture 44
Microclimates 55
Landscaping 59
Indoor Spaces 63
Sunspaces 67

PART FOUR - INDOOR AIR RISKS

Radon 79
Smoking 92
Airborne Particles 99
Indoor Combustion 104
Combustion Air 106
Thermal Systems 108
Chemicals 113
Spraying and Chlorofluorocarbons 121

PART FIVE - CARBON EMISSIONS

Petro-Powered Vehicles 127
Automotive Emissions 131
Fireplaces and Stoves 135

PART SIX - AIRBORNE OFFENDERS

Microorganisms 141
Swimming and Hot Spa Pools 143
Odors 148

PART SEVEN - INVISIBLE RADIATION

Radioactivity 153
Electromagnetic Energies 158
Geobiologic Energies 167

PART EIGHT - REMEDIES

Ventilation 173
Air Cleaning 192
Curtailing Waste and Air Pollution 214
The Reality 219
Our Larger Responsibility 223
Remedial Position 224

APPENDIX 227
REFERENCES 250
GLOSSARY 263

PART ONE - OVERVIEW

INTRODUCTION

Every home, building, or enclosed vehicle suffers from indoor air pollution. The indoor environment, in which we spend 80 to 90 percent of our time, is loaded with sources of serious air contamination. Indoor air pollution levels often exceed alert levels of outdoor air pollution.

We cannot live without air for more than a span of minutes, but we treat indoor air quality with relative indifference. The air quality in most homes and buildings ranges between fair to deplorable. Seldom are breathable qualities as good as would be desirable.

The primary source of indoor ventilation air is outdoor air. Our local and national concern focuses on the more visible brown clouds of urban air, while invisible toxic, electromagnetic, and radioactive risks of the indoor atmosphere remain largely ignored. Deplorable outdoor air pollution as well as attendant and more serious indoor air contamination require abatement of pollution sources and vast improvement by appropriate strategies.

Until **all sources** of indoor air risks, dangers, and lethal effects are identified and controlled, it is unlikely that our chemical, electromagnetic, and radioactive habitat will become less of a threat to ecological and human vitality and health. A change in the habits and responsibilities of business, industry, planners,

1

architects, designers, and people, as well as legal enactments, are critically essential to eliminate or effectively control these factors of life and well-being.

Our minds and bodies react in a total (holistic) way to biologic and psychologic insults and assaults. In like manner we can more effectively assure a more livable indoor environment, in which air is the major life giver, by considering the holistic and synergistic toxic and other biologic risk factors. **Source elimination** is the number-one strategy for well-being and health, but inasmuch as all pollution sources cannot be eliminated, the question gravitates to the most appropriate means of control.

The intent of this book is to create a level of awareness, delineate the possibilities and probabilities of risk, and propose strategies that can be applied to secure cleaner, more breathable air and a more livable, vitalizing indoor environment. As a source of information, reference, and application, it can serve professionals, educators, the public, and persons in government, politics, and business.

When a pollutant is attacked at the point of origin, it can be eliminated; once it is produced, it is too late.

-- Dr. Barry Commoner

THE INDOOR PROBLEM

Air is a precious and essential commodity. Without oxygen life would cease to exist. Toxic gases, irritating particulates, and radionuclides that concentrate within the indoor environment put us at risk. This risk is compounded by the multiple and synergistic effects of atmospheric pollutants.

On the risk side, homes and buildings encapsulate us within their interiors. Outdoor air (polluted to an extent) is our prime source of oxygen and indoor ventilation air. To polluted outdoor air we add our own indoor expired carbon dioxide, effluents from body wastes, and toxic fumes from smoking, cooking, operation of equipment, and other tasks and activities. These include cleaning, painting, artwork and craftwork, and other activities. Automobiles also contribute locally toxic emissions and fuel vapors that invade indoor space.

As a further imposition on health and vitality, the interior confines chemical gases and varied particulates from furnishings, furniture, clothing, possessions, printed material, interior surfaces, some health and beauty aids (!), solvents, chemicals, and household pets.

Invisible microorganisms that cause allergic reactions, illness, or death; invisible radionuclides from radon earth emissions; radioactivity from architectural materials; and very low, high, and ultra-high frequency electromagnetic radiation adversely impact our state of comfort, vitality, and health. In addition, recent work suggests that there may also be negative impacts from an absence of negative ionization, full-spectrum light, favorable electromagnetic fields, adequate indoor oxygenation, and salutary air temperatures and humidity.

Little is known about the synergistic biologic effects of this atmospheric onslaught. Less than adequate regulations, ordinances, or laws are in effect or exercised to control biologic and environmental risk. Until scientific and professional attention, more definitive research evaluations, assessment of risks, and procedures and strategies for abatement or control of indoor pollution are exercised, **appropriate precautions can be beneficially implemented within the framework of existing knowledge**.

Standards are critical to the process of control by means of legislation and need to be devised for resource, energy, construction, processes, and systems at the manufacturing level of materials, devices, and equipment. Consumer awareness, knowledge, and concern with indoor and outdoor air pollution, mitigation strategies, alternatives, and source elimination are conditions to meaningful societal change. Concern is developing. But critically needed is a "public mind with voice" as the effectual initiator for social and political relief from and elimination of these serious hazards.

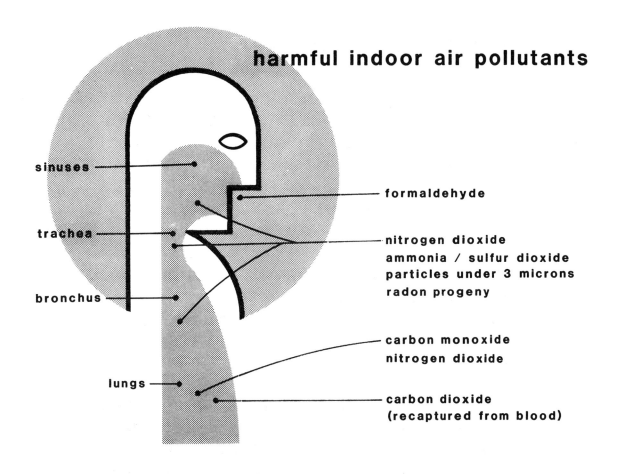

harmful indoor air pollutants

- sinuses
- trachea
- bronchus
- lungs

- formaldehyde
- nitrogen dioxide
  ammonia / sulfur dioxide
  particles under 3 microns
  radon progeny
- carbon monoxide
  nitrogen dioxide
- carbon dioxide
  (recaptured from blood)

Our respiratory system is at risk to the ever-changing concentrations and combinations of airborne toxins, particles, radionuclides, and microorganisms in our environs.

5

OUR TECHNO-SOCIETY

Our techno-society, without adequate policy guidelines or constraints, continues to drastically impair the global atmosphere. Local and global air pollution from vehicles and industry and the energy used for homes and buildings result in acid rain, the "greenhouse effect," destruction of the ozone layer, and a decimating effect upon natural ecosystems.

We are part and parcel of Nature. Our global techno-society with its fossil fuel, nuclear, and chemical base of energy and resources is rapidly undermining the livability and habitability of our planet. Our "artificial habitat" of homes, buildings, and enclosed vehicles and constituent networks that serve them deprecate our health and vitality.

Everything that we do, buy, or possess has an effect upon our personal environs. Furthermore, we create an attendant effect upon the global environment. Most of what we have and do is within the province of our fossil fuel technology. As we choose materials and systems for new buildings or remodelling, for products, processes, et al., we have a corresponding effect upon ourselves, upon others, and upon Nature's ecosystems.

The most environmentally sensitive and environmentally impaired members of society usually are first to suffer from anomalies of the environment. Each person is unique as to biophysical and psychoneural responses. The "true" effects of air pollution and contamination are often difficult to assess. In addition to our own physical and cerebral complexities, the environment has uncataloged and undefined layers of chemistry and other attributes that can subtract from ecologic and human vitality. Beyond our personal conscience, responsive and responsible accord with Nature, international policy, and legal regulations are needed to abate causes of pollution and preserve global ecosystems.

Federal or other regulations over indoor air quality are mainly nonexistent. While foodstuffs are substantially (but inadequately) regulated, the indoor atmosphere is subject to the whims of choice and chance. Public awareness, common concern, and our collective will are essential to instigate political regulation. Homes and buildings are composed of multifarious architectural and interior materials, equipment, and devices. Fluorescent lighting ballasts, appliances, televisions, computers, clocks, and other electrical and electronic equipment project adverse electromagnetic fields. Carpeting and vinyl floor coverings, paints, finishes, and other surfaces outgas various toxins. Radon that seeps up from the ground is a natural product, but needs to be reckoned with, along with other indoor insults to our health and biologic integrity.

We all remain part of the problem. If we want to live within a vital world with ecologic well-being and sustainability and with planetary ecosystems intact and functional, we have to examine our personal priorities and responsibilities.

Time is against us. Every moment of time adds an increment of deprecation and defilement to the global atmosphere. Gradualism may be too slow to effectually relieve Nature's ecologic distress. Waiting can be too late to essentially preserve our wondrous life-giving atmosphere and our magnificent planet. We need to not only be remedial, but also resourceful in averting and preventing subtle or overt injury to Nature's ecologic vitality and sustainability.

We can more readily relax with assurance when we reorder our techno-society in harmony and accord with natural processes. *Science and technology need a higher order of responsibility and sensitivity to the fragile parameters of Nature's ecosystems.*

SENSITIVITIES

Natural sensitivities have become atrophied in our technologically intensive society. The sensitivity to odor, taste, touch, sound, and vision is individual to each person. The deluge of aromas and distasteful odors that incessantly assail us in our chemical-laden society tends to lessen our sensory response. But strongly foul aromatic and pungent odors that accompany wafts of air are distressful to most persons.

The sensitivity of our nose can in measure protect us from many toxic and otherwise potentially harmful airborne pollutants. Persons with asthma, allergenic reactions, and other respiratory dysfunctions and children in particular need to exercise maximum caution in their exposure to prevalent harmful gases and particulates.

Unfortunately many potent pollutants, electromagnetic radiation, and radioactivity are not generally detectable by our ordinary senses. Few persons are able to sense invisible forms of radiation. An individual may be sensitive to airborne substances, geopathic energies (disturbed fields from the earth), or electromagnetic radiation from outdoor power lines or the internal wiring or transformers within a building. The influences might range from minor to severe impacts upon their health.

When the most sensitive and aware individuals are clearly stressed by physiologic or psychoneural responses to and debilities caused by environmental factors, we need to take heed. That which is revealed as having a countereffect upon the health and vitality of an ultra-sensitive individual can portend a similar fate for others. The total physiologic and psychologic stress load upon an individual is particularly difficult to assess. Inasmuch as life is dynamic and our personal responses are always within a changing state of receptivity, this further complicates diagnosis and appropriate remedies.

Not only do we need to educate the acute level of our sensory receptivity, which is possible to do with self- and programmed testing, but also to employ the most sensitive means of detection, whether by laboratory, equipment, or specialized devices. Self-education on the major and lesser aspects of air quality is a step in the protective direction.

We can increase our level of sensitivity by cultivating an awareness of odor, of what it is, its intensity, and from whence it is coming. Natural odors and chemical odors can become more distinguishable as we practice smelling. Detection of natural odors can warn us of pollens, spores, and processes of decay. Detection of chemical odors can warn us of petrochemical vapors and fumes, tobacco smoke, solvents, and a host of other products and substances that we encounter in our daily lives. Carpet, pad, and floor coverings carry no labels of content nor warning of chemical toxins. Paints and finishes also lack a definitive labelling of all ingredients. So it is with beauty aids, lotions, soaps, and items we find on most household shelves.

Detection by our sensitive awareness is the key to personal and collective well-being and survival. A "good nose" is a wonderful protective asset. It is possible to detect odors in concentrations as low as 0.2 parts per trillion. Nevertheless, we need awareness as well as action against the dangers from technological and natural sources. As we <u>learn</u> to sharpen our sense of smell, we enhance our degree of sensitivity. We also improve our choice and chance in avoidance of harm.

Environmental illnesses (EI) have escalated within our artificial environments loaded with products, systems, and energies that are counter to health and well-being. As infectious diseases that decimated human life in the past have been conquered, environmental sensitivities and illnesses are becoming the new frontier of clinical ecology, health, and medical practice.

BREATHING

We can survive without eating for about a month, water for about a week, but in not breathing death is only minutes away. The vital gas exchange between our lungs and bloodstream is a day and night continuum of needed oxygenation from air.

The atmosphere contains 21 percent oxygen that prevails at a remarkably sustained level. The atmosphere, predominantly nitrogen, also contains carbon dioxide, helium, hydrogen, the rare gases argon, krypton, xenon, and neon, as well as a host of less than desirable particles and pollutants.

When we breathe, we breathe what our localized air has to offer. Under normal unstressed breathing, adults breathe in about 500 milliliters of air 14 times per minute (7 liters of air per minute). Under the stress of physical activity this can increase to over 120 liters per minute. Millions of alveoli and pulmonary capillaries within the lung are thin enough for gas transfer to occur to the bloodstream. Oxygen is picked up and carbon dioxide is expelled.

Our respiratory system is a wondrous organic filtration and defense system. As air enters our nasal passages, it encounters small hairlike cilia that have a waving motion. The cilia, aided by sticky mucus, capture and sweep particulates, bacteria, and viruses down into the throat, where they pass down through the esophagus and are expelled by our digestive system. In particular, bacteria and other microorganisms are killed by stomach acids. Others that survive and get into the bloodstream are met by our body's inner defenses of macrophages, white blood cells, T cells, and B cells.

The bronchial tree of our lungs also contains cilia and mucus-forming tissue that function to contain and expel the irritants and micro-invaders of our respiratory system. We are at risk to the extent that our respiratory filtration and defense fall short of meeting the physical invasion and biologic insults.

Humidity plays a critical role in our respiratory encounter with the atmosphere. When airborne humidity exceeds 60 percent or is less than 40 percent, exposure to microorganic bacteria and viruses that proliferate more abundantly under such conditions becomes more of an invasive threat. Humidity is also salutary to the effective functioning of our cilia. It aids the cilia's protective action against particulates of natural or synthetic origin, as well as living or dead microorganisms.

Respiratory vulnerability does not evenly prevail in our population. Individuals with respiratory diseases and allergic tendencies are at particular risk from air pollution, contaminants, and ineffective oxygenation. Everyone is subject to the probabilities of respiratory stress, distress, and debility within the polluted confines of the indoor environment.

In an average life span (70 years) we breathe 500 million to 1 billion times. The quality of the air we breathe intimately affects our personal state of health and vitality.

To have "clean" oxygenated air is not enough. A cogent question is, "how vital is the air?" Nature's composition of air with oxygen, predominant nitrogen, and trace increments of helium, argon, krypton, neon, and xenon actively vitalized with ionizing and electro fields is conducive to our respiratory and biological vitality. Filtration alone with HEPA (high-efficiency particulate air) filters removing over 99 percent of air impurities results in essentially "clean" but "non-vital" air.

Air is "vital" when it has a bioneural and physiologic balance of negative ions (a median level of 3,000 to 6,000 .001 micron ions per cubic centimeter per second) and positive ion concentrations at less than half the negative ions. Workplace environs due to rapid grounding off on equipment, ductwork, lighting, and processes may require a median level of 10,000 to 15,000 negative ions in the same range.

OXYGEN

All terrestrial and aquatic life depends on oxygen. Atmospheric oxygen is produced by phytoplankton of the oceans, terrestrial and aquatic vegetation, and bacterial processes.

Our human assault upon the earth's atmosphere, land, and waterways boomerangs into an assault upon our primary need for breathing, with a concomitant effect upon our total organic vitality.

Acidic atmospheric moisture particles descend as acid rain, which retards and kills vegetation, alters aquatic and terrestrial ecosystems, and can corrode building materials. It is produced by emissions from industry and gasoline-powered vehicles in the form of sulfur dioxide and nitrous oxides that mix with atmospheric moisture. The corrosive character of our noxious airborne effluents is no respecter of respiratory health.

There is little scientific probability that we will run out of oxygen on a global scale. But our total national consumption of oxygen most likely exceeds that which is generated from our territorial waters, forests, and other vegetation. The oxygen demand of our vehicles and for industrial, household, and other combustion needs is met by global sources beyond the limitation of our national sources. The world situation is further exacerbated by the destruction of tropical forests and global vegetation and by declining oxygenation from the seas. On a global basis, one acre of forest is lost every second.

Global economic rewards are needed to stem the depletion of forests, loss of vegetation, and devitalization of the seas. It is a paradox that more oxygen used for efficient combustion to decrease pollution will further deplete the oxygen of our global atmosphere.

In accidents and for certain emergencies "pure" oxygen is administered for recovery. In the unfortunate inhalation of industrial chemical gases, victims are given oxygen treatment. Athletes may "beef up" the oxygen in their blood by a supply during a contest. But these are uncommon temporary or emergency administrations. The curious factor is that oxygen (O and O_2) is essential to life, but ozone (O_3) can be injurious to our lungs. Ozone is a potent bactericide and is used for air and water purification. Caution is advised in the handling and use of oxygen. It is highly compressed in cylinders and strongly supports combustion.

A "fresh air" mixture that duplicates "pure" oxygenated air should be available for personal or room-size application. Many of us seek out "pure" bottled water or filter out the noxious contaminants from a municipal supply. Space capsules need a "fresh air" mix compatible with Nature's atmospheric formula. "Fresh air" retreat spaces within a home, hospital, workplace, health club, or other location could do much to relieve respiratory stress. Aerobics are popular, but does anyone question the <u>quality</u> of the air most suited to such beneficial exercise?

Packaged "pure air" units might become a handy item for a bioneural "pickup" as needed. But no matter how "pure," the air will not be vital without active ionization. Highly efficient room-type filtration systems can clean up the air, but they do not provide oxygen renewal nor the vitalization of the air. An effectual selection of the most oxygenating plants may well be part of the "fresh air" environs.

Persons in a closed space, depending upon interior air volume, the number of persons, and their degree of activity, can in time substantially elevate carbon dioxide (CO_2) levels. Carbon dioxide has no odor. But in an enclosed environment we may notice a "stuffiness" or define a sense of "stale air." The carbon dioxide concentration in air is usually about .03 percent. Carbon dioxide triggers the breathing response. With increasing concentrations fatigue, headaches, and drowsiness can occur. At concentrations over 10 percent unconsciousness can result and lead to death by suffocation. Ventilation with outdoor air and indoor air ionization are the remedies for oxygen-depleted and devitalized indoor air.

While oxygenated air is essential, its biologic significance is considerably enhanced by its symbiotic accord with ionization. Because they are present in the natural atmosphere, rare air gases may also play a role of biologic value.

Every cell of our body bears the need of oxygen and the ability through our blood and organic detoxifiers to eliminate physiologic and toxic offenders. Our biologic efficiency in using oxygen depends upon the vitality and receptivity of our respiratory system and on our circulatory and metabolic functions. What and when we eat and drink, exercise, use supplements and medications, and our psychoneural and physiologic state affect our oxygen utilization.

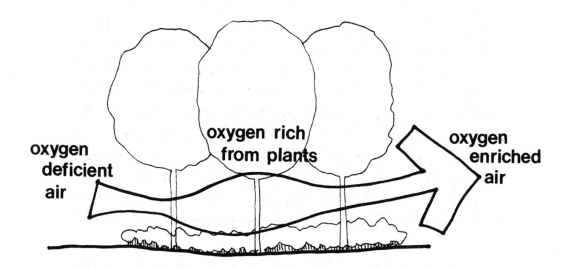

PART TWO - BIOLOGIC EFFECTS

BIOLOGIC STRESS

Our biologic stress is increased as odoriferous, irritating, and toxic airborne substances and contaminants become more concentrated. The duration of exposure, synergistic compounding, proximity to the source, direction of air flow, and other inherent mind and body stresses result in a total stress burden.

Personal olfactory sensitivity as well as sensory conditioning to prevailing odors and irritants play a role in our perceptual tolerance. Various physical barriers of the architectural interior, furnishings, furniture, planting, and people can, depending upon the patterns of ventilation, attenuate or intercept and redirect the offending contaminants away from or towards us.

Primary remedies are elimination of the pollutant source, effective ventilation, dilution within a large interior air volume, controlled air convection patterns, filtration, ionization, interception, and effective barriers. The type, persistence, and intensity of the source have a fundamental bearing upon levels of air pollution, environmental contamination, and attendant biologic risk.

The ultimate defense we have against the weight of biologic stress, if remedies are not exercised, is the vital integrity of our cells and our physiologic and psychologic fortuity. Each person is at risk in measure to the singular, synergistic, or multiple stressors and their level of effective biologic resistance.

When our respiratory system is overstressed, our cerebral, cardiovascular, and immune functions are subject to concomitant stress. Office productivity and other activities can consequently decline. Therefore in the workplace, the employer can benefit by reductions in absenteeism, dysfunction, and in some cases legal liabilities by providing "clean air" environs. Our immunologic defense system benefits by clean, vital air.

Children are particularly sensitive to air pollution. The National Heart and Lung Institute notes that children exposed to air pollution can suffer greater immunological impairment than an adult, due to their higher metabolic rate and greater activity levels. A "safe" level is individualistic to each child. Inasmuch as children inhale two to three times more airborne pollutants per unit of body weight than an adult, they are more subject to physiologic as well as mental illness.

Air pollution at all ages has been noted to initiate immunological disorders such as asthma, increased respiratory tract infections, reduction in pulmonary function, and cardiopulmonary or other diseases. Sulfur dioxide, ozone, and nitrogen dioxide are potent bronchoconstrictors. Automobiles in particular contribute to ozone. Recent data from Bell Communications Research show that indoor concentrations of ozone can exceed 70 percent of outdoor levels when smog ozone was sucked in through ventilation systems. The greater the rate of ventilation, the higher was the incidence of ozone. Persons with respiratory problems, children, and people engaged in strenuous activities are at particular risk from this respiratory irritant.

Free Radicals

The cells of our body are assaulted by "free radicals" from numerous sources. Free radicals are molecules that have an unpaired electron. These highly reactive free radicals try to pair with other molecules and can cause extensive cellular damage by penetration of the outer cell membrane, protein structures, and genetic materials. They can be the precursor of some types of cancer and other degenerative diseases.

Some causes of free radicals include polynuclear aromatic hydrocarbons (produced from burning organic materials such as wood, coal, oil, and tobacco), aldehydes (chemical pollutants from cigarettes, auto exhaust, and smog), radiation, ultraviolet light, and possibly prolonged strenuous exercise and stress.

Free radical damage can be limited by certain antioxidant nutrients that scavenge free radicals from our cells or prevent their harmful action. The most prominent of these are vitamins C and E, betacarotene (a substance related to vitamin A), and the mineral selenium.

BIOLOGIC RESISTANCE

The question is not only how to purify and vitalize indoor air, but also how persons within the indoor environment can improve their biologic resistance to biophysical deprecation within a less than salutary environment.

A state of general good health is always beneficial to our inner processes of biologic defense and regeneration. Increasing our resistance to biologic insults is a peak need under the exponential risks we now bear.

Our immune system is a bulwark against illness, incapacity, and death. The air we continually breathe and all of Nature's other environmental elements bolster or undermine our immune system. Our senses are a warning system to the hazards of our environs. But the unseen and unsensed inner workings of the immune system are a formidable defense against airborne and other organic and inorganic assailants.

A prime question is, how can we strengthen our immune responses to protect us against the incessant attack of microorganisms, particulates, noxious gases, and our ingestion of radionuclides and harmful substances in food and water? Avoidance, elimination, and removal of environmental offenders are beneficial steps. But how can we sidestep our continual exposure to the overwhelming multilevel anti-biologic reality? The answer is that we can eliminate or otherwise control the aberrant factors in our environs. The more we can lessen their burden, the better chance our immune system can protect us.

Smoking has become anti-social instead of its former place as a social habit. Cigarette smoke has a contrary effect upon the immune system. The synergistic effect of chemicals, cigarette smoke, radioactivity, and electromagnetism compounds the impact upon our immune response. Fortunately more and more municipalities, some states, and governmental and private businesses are initiating "smoke free" areas.

The stronger and more "in-depth" resistive our immune system is (with less environmental impacts), the better is our chance of keeping well and healthy. Our body reacts in a holistic (total) manner to the ever-changing aspects of our environs. Holistic health is the safest route to a continuing state of wellness and biologic vitality.

For yourself, take an "air breathing inventory" by day, by week, by month. Critically evaluate the air where you spend your time at home, work, shopping, play, or whatever. Think about the air when you are there. How does it seem to affect you as to odor, freshness, smoke, toxins, air movement, and as to your comfortable inhalation or degree of respiratory stress or distress? If you are with someone, ask them how they react. Or you can always talk to people in a space with questionable air quality and find out their reaction and the effect upon them.

As previously stated, in most buildings the air quality ranges from fair to deplorable. As we all become "air sleuths" and learn to be more sensitively alert and astutely aware of the air of different environs, we can more readily recognize what the specific offenders of air quality may be and then firmly voice our concerns to persons who can be directly instrumental in correction of the condition.

The workplace is fraught with biologic hazards. Occupational air quality standards set by government agencies (usually for industrial situations) often fail to be enforced, are not adequately inclusive of many singular and interactive toxins and particulates, and are often subverted by the industry or business in which they prevail. So many processes and products not under government regulation are counter to immunological well-being.

Ample safety margins are needed in establishing National Ambient Air Quality Standards for indoor and outdoor air to protect our entire population. In-depth clinical research and studies are needed to more clearly determine and document the parameters of biologic harm caused by atmospheric stressors.

Our environment where we live, work, and play has both a subtle and overt effect upon our physical and mental being. We are the sum total of our thought processes and physical vitalities. The air we continually breathe is primary to that vitality. As we learn to improve our sensitivities and enhance our immune system, we can better our state of vitality. Freedom from dysfunction depends upon the total state of our health, and the indoor and outdoor atmosphere attends all the moments of our life. "Clean vital air" is the bottom line.

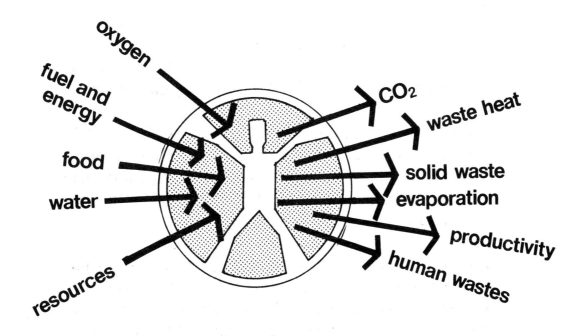

man's inputs and outputs

BIOSYSTEMS

Growing trees, shrubs, grasses, and other plants are bio-oxygenators, bio-filters, and bio-ionizers. Vegetation that grows rapidly, with extensive leaf surfaces, is especially capable of converting CO_2 to O_2 and in measure oxygenating the air. Trees can remove impurities from the air by trapping particles on their leaves, branches, and stems and by absorbing many gaseous and other pollutants directly into their leaves. Pine needles and other pointed-leaf plants give off negative ions through the points, thereby charging airborne particulates in such a manner that they are grounded off to nearby surfaces. They also act as a direct endocrine stimulant as we breathe negative-ionized air into our lungs. Our brain serotonin level is reduced and our awareness level is increased by the effect of negative ions on our respiratory and circulatory systems. Elevated serotonin levels tend to lead us toward sleep.

Extensive indoor planting in attached greenhouses or atria can be used for oxygen and humidification in conjunction with solar heating and inductive ventilation systems. They can also be located on the return side of forced-air mechanical systems as a prefilter for the absorption of carbon dioxide. Plants that most effectively absorb CO_2 and oxygenate the air should be selected.

The oxygen output from indoor plants is very small. But spider plants that grow prolifically with little care act as effective conditioners of indoor air. They grow well in pots, and in hanging baskets they will cascade down with many new shoots. These can be cut to begin new plants. Researchers at the John Stennis Space Center in Mississippi estimate that in the average home, 15 spider plants could remove the formaldehyde emissions from furniture, walls, and cooking. Aloe vera and philodendron plants were also found to reduce levels of formaldehyde, benzene, and carbon dioxide.

A collaborative effort of NASA (National Aeronautic and Space Administration) and ALCA (Associated Landscape Contractors of America) is directed towards using plants within the indoor environment to "clean up" contaminated air.

The question is whether selected plants can meet the complex task of biodegrading particulates, fungi, and bacteria and possibly lowering radon levels within work environs. A NASA/ALCA experiment is testing the ability of 14 houseplants to remove three volatile organic chemicals: benzene, trichloroethylene (TCE), and formaldehyde, which are suspected of contributing to "sick building syndrome." All the plants scavenged the pollutants to some extent, but their effectiveness was variable. Preliminary results suggest that one 10-to 12-inch potted plant per 100 square feet of floor space could significantly reduce low-level organic chemical pollution. Fan-driven plant filters have been developed that also can be used to clean indoor air. The roots of plants (in a surround of activated carbon acting as a filter) act to biodegrade large airborne particle contaminants (with attendant microorganisms aiding the process) using a blower to bring them to the roots. Commercial versions of these plant filters should be on the market soon. The leaves, but more so the roots, of plants appear to be able to degrade the pathogenic contaminants of indoor air.

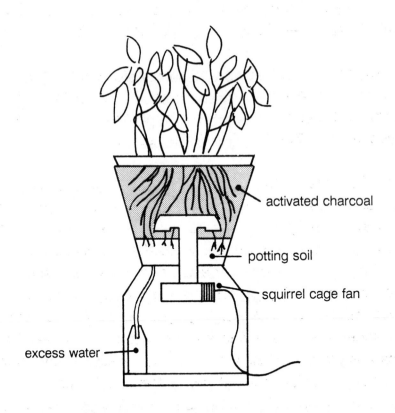

NASA's concept of an indoor air purification system that combines plants and activated charcoal.

"SICK BUILDING SYNDROME"

Most often with new office buildings and office renovations, symptomatic complaints of occupants have to do with indoor air. A variety of symptoms, including headaches, fatigue, infections, neurological and psychological disorders, irritability, forgetfulness, burning of the eyes and throat, and abnormal absenteeism, are associated with "sick building syndrome." Usually these symptoms do not fit the pattern of any particular illness and are difficult to trace to any specific source.

Offices of all types where persons are enclosed and directly isolated from the outdoor atmosphere are subject to aberrant physiologic and psychoneural conditions. The air quality of the majority of office or other types of building occupancy falls below the line of adequacy. Air changes per hour (ACH) of intake ventilation are often less than commensurate with the relative toxicity of the indoor environs. Outgassing from building materials and contents, copy machines, and other equipment contributes to adverse health effects.

"Sick building syndrome" is associated with ventilation systems with inadequate outdoor air intake, designed to conserve energy in tightly sealed structures. Most of the air is recirculated to save on fuel costs, often with replacement rates of only 5 to 10 percent. Ductwork is often found to be a source of proliferating biological contaminants. Ducts can also be blocked as much as 70 percent by dirt, dust, and hydrocarbon deposits from cooking and automobile exhaust. In fact, many times air intake ducts are located near loading docks where idling diesel trucks contaminate the air with hydrocarbon fumes and carbon monoxide.

Air moving through HVAC (heating, ventilating, air conditioning) ductwork grounds off beneficial negative ionization, resulting in residual positive ions. Nearly all interiors lack desirable negative ionization that vitalizes the air and stimulates our endocrine system. The most prevalent indoor condition in homes and other buildings is one in which positive ionized particles cling to interior surfaces and are suspended in the air. Positive ions have a negative effect upon our alertness, health, and vitality and encourage bacterial growth.

A potpourri of indoor materials, activities (including smoking if allowed), and odors plus adverse electromagnetic fields emanating from equipment put a concomitant stress upon the occupants. The indoor environment is populated by a diverse cross section of persons with individual habits, routines, and sensitivities. Cleaning up the indoor environs is usually a multifaceted task. More than a single contaminant can require attention. Isolating nefarious causes calls upon a "detective" mentality. Psychologic and well as physiologic factors can be symptomatic.

Another element that can have a contrary biologic effect is the geopathic energies of the earth. Studies in Germany of the effect of geopathic and cosmic energies upon building occupants have been made. Findings indicate that high-rise buildings of concrete and steel have a deleterious bio-effect in their tendency to concentrate geopathic anomalies (disturbed fields) in higher floors and to intercept and slow cosmic rays from outer space to where they can on lower floors have an undesired impact upon the cells of our body.

An intensive effort should be made to find and eliminate all "sources" that cause the "sick building syndrome" or that possibly contribute to the biologic problem. Another tack can be intervention by controlled negative ion generation coupled with Schumann positive field resonance or electron field generation to benefit indoor air quality and provide vital indoor ionization. All floor coverings, furniture, furnishings, equipment (computer, reproduction, and other subject to electromagnetism and outgassing), systems, processes, wall and ceiling finishes, as well as the contents, including materials used in the course of work, should be considered as to their effect on indoor air quality. At the personal level smoking, perfumes, colognes, clothing, and body odors add to the total atmospheric pollution.

Comparative "sick building" investigative studies in Europe have been made with and without occupants in the building. Building "causes" can more readily be determined by closely controlled monitoring of steady-state interior conditions. A question then exists as to the effect of workplace activities upon the building occupants versus problem factors of the building itself and its specific contents. Reduction of variables in any study of "problems" is conducive to an effective solution.

The "artificial" environs of most workplaces is antithetic to our vital need for a sensory connection with earth, sky, and atmosphere. As we release tensions by our correspondence with the flux of daylight, invigorated air, and the natural field pulse energies of the earth, our vital psychoneural and physiologic responses are enhanced.

A question gets back to the architect, interior designer, and mechanical engineer as to a coordinated effort to achieve a healthful as well as comfortable and aesthetic indoor environment. The total indoor environment as to the architecture, natural and mechanical systems relative to occupant activities, and all other contributory factors affect workplace efficiency. Indoor air studies are being made by the Environmental Protection Agency, Department of Energy, and various universities. Honeywell Indoor Air Diagnostics in an extensive study covering indoor environmental conditions found that about 20% of workers identified air problems as reducing their work performance.

In all cases in which indoor air problems are not readily controlled or eliminated, a professional analyst experienced with aero-biologic distress and dysfunction should be engaged to find solutions to the aberrant condition. Sensitive portable equipment is available for evaluating the indoor atmosphere.

When a solution is reached, consistent monitoring and cleaning of ductwork, HVAC equipment, or other devices that affect indoor air quality can be crucial to workplace health, comfort, and productivity. Nonallergenic and nontoxic cleaning methods and materials for maintenance of indoor work spaces should be a priority.

Depending upon air problems encountered, corrected, or apt to reoccur, a person experienced with occupational systemic monitoring should be employed to oversee functions of the building in regard to possible related dysfunctions of its occupants.

PART THREE - OUR ENVIRONS

BUILT ENVIRONMENT

Existing homes and buildings with their supportive roadway and utility networks comprise most of our built environment. It is an "artificial systemic habitat" that we have imposed upon Nature's earthly domain. For the most part today's architectural designs and constructions neglect an ecologic harmony with Nature. Atmospheric patterns of climate, site-specific air movement, and effectual ventilation for health and vitality too often are not evident in the original concept of planning and design. Indigenous architecture through various historic periods expressed a conscious agreement with Nature. Climatology was part of the conceptual equation.

Stylism has had a way of submerging the connection between humankind and the natural scale, form, and energies of a specific site. Most of our built architecture is an irrelevant collection of eclectic styles. Orientation to daily and seasonal patterns of wind, sun, and air temperatures and the beneficent effect of natural energies upon the occupants are neglected. A fortuitous link among a verdant setting, the outdoor atmosphere and sky, and indoor spaces is rarely present in site planning and landscaping.

Older homes and buildings are more or less unique candidates for site replanning and architectural modifications for solar and natural indoor ventilation and cooling. Older homes and buildings and their furnishings are likely to harbor molds, dust, mites, and other microorganisms that can offend our respiratory system. Old forced-air or gravity ductwork heating systems can aggravate breathing problems. Cleaning the ducts and installing effective filters can bring relief.

Older homes are most likely to have gas-fired furnaces and hot water tanks that draw their combustion air from indoor spaces. As homes are made "tight" to conserve energy, the furnace should be separately and "tightly" enclosed (according to code and fire safety) from indoor living spaces, and outdoor air should directly or by a duct be installed to provide combustion air. A more efficient alternative is to replace an old furnace (possibly only 40 to 45 percent efficient) with a new one (over 80 percent efficient) provided with direct outside combustion air.

"Tight" construction will reduce and could nearly eliminate the sieve-like infiltration of outdoor air around doors, windows, and the building envelope. An added sunspace, air-to-air heat exchanger, or other controlled introduction of tempered ventilation air can be important.

Radon is apt to be encountered in levels above 4 picocuries per liter (pCi/l) and could become very serious under conditions of "tight" renovation. Measures taken should be appropriate to meet the severity of the problem. Commercial and institutional building renovations have their own unique ventilation and air quality problems that require special attention and design solutions.

In the interest of energy conservation, conservation of resources, and avoiding the environmental impact of new construction, the preservation and energy-conscious redesign of older buildings can reduce air pollution. The built environment offers a particular opportunity for home and building owners, architects, and building designers.

Upgrading the air quality of indoor spaces; using nontoxic and nonallergenic materials, finishes, equipment, and furnishings; and exercising control over radon and electromagnetic energies in renovation are needed directions.

LOCATION AND AIR QUALITY

Where we live, work, play, or may otherwise decide to spend our time is critical to indoor air quality and our health.

+ Locate homes and buildings to minimize the impact of outdoor air pollution.
+ Locate in a city, town, or county that has minimal air pollution.
+ Locate on a hill rather than a valley where pollution is more apt to concentrate.
+ Do not locate near a major highway or traffic intersection.
+ Do not locate next to a parking lot.
+ Do not locate downwind from a power plant, chemical plant, or nuclear processing plant.
+ Do not locate near industrial operations.
+ Do not locate near local businesses that exhaust pollutants.
+ Do not locate near a railroad line that carries hazardous materials.
+ Do not locate near airfields.
+ Do not locate on land farmed with pesticides and chemical fertilizers.
+ Locate away from agricultural fields that are sprayed.
+ Do not live under or near high-voltage power lines.
+ Locate away from stagnant waterways.
+ Locate out of air pollution or "seepage" range of oil or gas wells.
+ Locate a safe distance from any mining operations.

+ Locate close to a park, near a forest, or within a natural setting.
+ Locate in a small healthful rural or seacoast community.
+ Consider the effect of altitude upon air quality.
+ Consider prevailing diurnal and seasonal wind patterns.
+ Before moving to a city, review an air quality record of the past several years.
+ In urban or rural locations, consider sites for passive solar orientation and exposure.
+ South-sloping sites are preferable for drainage and solar advantage.
+ Avoid being in a "shadow path" during winter months in a cold climate.
+ Avoid sites with high levels of radon or other radioactivity.
+ Before buying a property, get soils, radon, and water tests (if a well is planned).
+ Check municipal water quality.

All of these locational ideals are unlikely to be met. But these concerns provide a basis for locational evaluation.

ECOLOGIC ARCHITECTURE

Ecologic architecture originates from conceptual and evaluative design that is in harmony with Nature's ecologic vitality. It is architecture that respectfully obeys site-specific energies of sun, air, earth, and water. Ecologic architecture is sensitive to and focused upon our biologic wellness and vitality given by cosmic forces that animate Nature.

The indoor atmosphere as a fractional part of the global atmosphere sustains our life and vitality as companion to the virtues of sun, earth, and water. Within the holistic concept and design of plan and form, the solar, atmospheric, and ecologic specifics of the site determine the design. Diurnal and seasonal design coherence to the microclimate is essential.

As a living and dependent part of Nature, our factors of health and vitalization have an intimate bond with Nature's microclimatic ecologic vitality. Instead of our dominance <u>over</u>, our <u>obedience</u> to natural flows of air within the site and architectural interior can find accord with the daily penetrations of skyvault illumination and the light and interior thermal convection from direct solar radiation.

The formative materials, means, and methods of the architecture should place the <u>least</u> demand upon indigenous natural ecosystems. All materials in respect to Nature and our health and vitality should be free of toxicity and avoid atmospheric pollution as to source, transport, and energies of incorporation into the structure. Self-sufficiency by sun, air, earth, and water heating, cooling, and ventilation and *in situ* photovoltaic solar electric generation is a worthy realization.

Ecologic architecture requires an adaptable, dynamic perspective. It is a container of the atmosphere, a division of interior space, a penetrated envelope by daylight and sun, and a protector of person and possessions. It is the most fixed element of the living equation. All the forces of Nature, her micro and other organic creatures, vegetation, and our own excursions and ventures in space are dynamic. The more that architecture in concept, planning, and design can correspond with our own ecologic dynamic and that of Nature, the more it will be effective as a vital and living environ.

Climate-responsive solar and ecologic architecture harks back to ancient times. Our scientific, technologic, and societal perspective of today is in clear need of a return to this ancient ecologic view. A marriage between new revelations in the physics of basic matter and energy, metaphysics, constituents of architecture, and our part within the ecologic scheme is primal to our human vitality, sustainability, and survival. Ecologic architecture today requires an ethical alignment with and obedience to Nature. Architecture is a creative and inventive profession and within an ecologic ethic, new forms and certain historic concepts can usher in new resolutions.

Health, vitality, and sustainability remain key to ecologic concept and design, the ecologic bond between site and architecture, and the holistic energy dynamics of Nature's atmosphere, climatology, and inspirited energies in concert with the sun.

Ecologic architecture envisions ecologic responsibility conferred upon the architect and designer of site, architecture, and interior. Ecologic design evolves out of Nature's site-specific energies in economic coherence with our biologic needs and behavioral patterns. As with Nature, the design grows and forms from within.

As an interface between interior and exterior space occurs in planning, the exterior architecture is born. In its modelling to the forces of sun, air, earth, and water, an economic effectiveness and harmony is attained with the atmosphere and the earth.

Ecologic architecture is a long-term investment that provides healthful living by all means, methods, and realizations of the site that are conducive to the well-being of the occupants. "Healthy home" is a common term that relates to our human ecology and state of wellness. But to be fully "ecologic," architecture must not only respect Nature's ecosystems and ecosystemic energies but also align with the *in situ* optimal use of sun, air, earth, and water energies and accord with all site-specific and neighboring conditions. From concept to the completion of a project, frugality in the use of resources and energies must accompany the construction process and energy self-sustainability be the ultimate objective.

A "holistic" view within a full responsibility of what is planned, designed, and specified is essential. To preserve and most wisely use our planet's resources and energies initially in construction and through the life-cycle of the project is fundamental to ecologic design.

There are diverse opinions about what construction methods and materials constitute an ecologic, "healthy home." Common objectives (for the most part) are as follows:

+ to avoid plastic or other materials made of toxic ingredients and by toxic processes that harmfully outgas in the indoor environs;

+ use of nontoxic natural materials in preference to synthetic materials;

+ design concern for sensitive individuals as well as for healthy, visibly less affected individuals subject to biologic or psychoneural disturbance, distress, or dysfunction;

+ concern that Nature's ecologic sustainability and well-being should not be diminished by what is built; and

+ a responsibility to conceive, design, build, and furnish a home or building to a "healthy home" ecologic ethic.

Beyond these fundamentals, the author would add:

+ avoidance of all energy-intensive materials, means, and methods that pollute and cause environmental damage;

+ optimize the use of site-specific energies of sun, earth, air, and water;

+ preserve the natural ecosystems of the site and its microorganic vitality;

+ with landforming and landscaping make the microclimate of the site more gentle;

+ correspond climate-responsive architecture with landforms and landscaping;

+ the architecture, site, and interior should be a self-sustaining energy system for outdoor space use and indoor comfort and well-being;

+ create a marriage between the architectural interior and the outdoors of sky, earth, and vegetation;

+ employ skyvault and direct solar daylighting and thermal radiation of the interior in accord with diurnal and seasonal space use and comfort;

+ use the sun's energy for biologic vitality, direct and retained heating, air tempering, and aesthetic pleasure;

+ plan and design the architecture to human biology and psychoneural responses and to human activities, tasks, relaxation, and behavior;

+ design for frugality and local sources of materials, means, methods, and use of "clean" energies;

+ use on-site and local resources and energies in preference to those from a distance;

+ defensive design against site and local intensities of air pollution from vehicles or other sources;

+ defensive design against intruders and for practical security;

+ climatic interior and outdoor space planning that benefits by conditions of the day as well as season to conserve energy and agree with human activities;

+ architecture, site, and interior planned for time-frame adaptability, privacy, self-sufficiency, and minimal maintenance;

+ avoidance of adverse electromagnetic, radioactive, and geopathic energies; and

+ specification of materials, devices, and equipment is critical to air quality.

There is a tendency to overlook the fact that <u>what we build with and how we build it</u> are as important as how we use a home or building after it is finished.

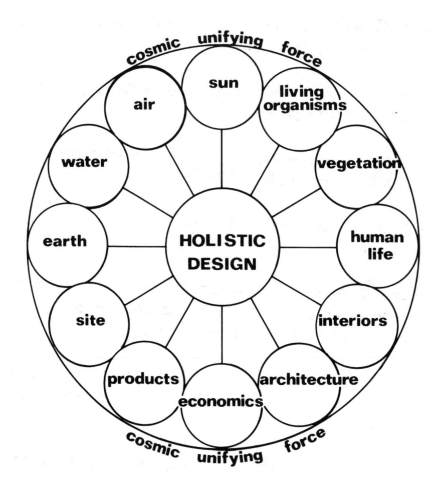

Ecologic Communities

Ecologic communities as new development or as a redesign of existing communities are essential to the renewal and preservation of Nature's living and cyclic ecosystems. Subdivisions have to be viewed and studied in a new and complete way. The existing built environment and its infrastructure and energy networks require an ambitious perspective devoted to atmospheric vitality and Nature's ecosystemic vitality.

The guidelines for new developments for homes, buildings, and our own ecologic preservation are set forth below.

+ Land evaluation and planning to minimize roadways and create a site most amenable to optimal initial and life-cycle community and architecture energy conservation.

+ Site planning to optimize site-specific benefits of sun, air, earth, and water energies.

+ Evaluation and preservation of the prevailing natural ecology. Preserve and reuse topsoil with its microorganic life. Protect existing trees and vegetation during the construction process.

+ Prime objectives for community and individual properties are to be self-sufficient and self-sustaining with internalized integration of energies.

+ Avoid harmful electromagnetic and radioactive emanations.

+ Emphasis on a park-like community with organic gardening outdoors and efficient design of greenhouses.

+ Avoidance of high allergenic varieties of trees and plants.

+ Conservation of roof and surface water for irrigation.

+ Concrete (instead of asphalt) for streets, driveways, and parking areas.

+ Avoidance of auto fumes from street and garage entering homes.

+ Site-specific microclimatic landforming and landscaping to attenuate climatic extremes and condition the atmosphere.

+ Optimizing outdoor and roof space use.

+ Climate-responsive all-season architectural design.

+ Use of roofing and exterior materials that are inert.

+ Envelope form and details of the architecture to control outdoor air movement and optimize indoor air ventilation.

+ Use methods to avert radon and other soil gases.

+ Openings as to type, size, and location for most effective interior daylighting and passive solar gain.

+ Interior planning as to functional, physiologic, and psychologic air quality space use, daylighting, and thermal factors.

+ Architecture to function as a natural energy system for thermal comfort, heating, cooling, air tempering, humidification, and ventilation.

+ Design, specify, and construct with nonpolluting materials, equipment, means, methods, and finishes.

+ Priority use of renewable and *in situ* resources and energy. Avoidance of petro-based resources, energies, and products.

+ Avoid, eliminate, transform, or recycle all initial and life-cycle waste.

+ Eliminate or minimize mechanical systems, devices, and equipment.

+ Seek low and high tech solutions most appropriately aligned with Nature's ecosystemic vitality and sustainability.

+ Use nonallergenic, nontoxic, nonpolluting constituents for architecture and interior furnishings.

<u>The bottom line</u>: a community and architecture that place the least demand upon polluting resources and energies and are in accord with Nature's and our own vitality.

MICROCLIMATES

There are many climates within the continental United States and many microclimates within each regional climate. Site-specific microclimates can have greater fluctuations in character and temperature than those which prevail regionally.

Air quality is notably affected by the influences of each specific site. Wind patterns, topography, vegetation, architecture, and other features of the site and its surroundings all have an effect upon air quality. Regional architecture in a general way fits a region's seasonal climatology. Regionalism is more reasonable than imported, incongruous architectural stylism and divisive eclectic architecture. But site-specific attributes and character of the land, the sun, water, and sky and site-specific microclimatic solar architecture fit more closely within an ecologic and conservation concern.

Ecologic architectural design of homes and buildings to fit best with the microclimate of the site is in the direction of self-sufficiency. As we optimize the use of site-specific energies, we gain the benefit of a "cleaner" atmosphere and a climate more gentle and compatible with natural ecosystems and ourselves.

Outdoor microclimates where we may spend time and the indoor microclimates within rooms and other spaces affect our sensory responses. As we move about or remain in a fixed position, the air moves about us. We are always in contact with the air, with surfaces, with levels of sound, and with our visual response to light, form, color, and texture. The air brings to us or we move through various fields of pleasant, benign, or disturbing odors. Our mobility and level of responsive sensitivity can motivate us to move to a pleasant spot or to escape from one that offends our sense of smell and psychophysical responses.

As we migrate from space to space or from one environment to another, we are exposed to variant levels of air pollution. Whether at home, in the workplace, or elsewhere, we are confronted by atmospheric conditions of diverse micro environs. Not only can we conserve energy and improve our environs by our treatment of outdoor and indoor micro environs, but we also benefit our health and vitality as we use caution in controlling our environmental exposure.

The steps we can take in ecologic microclimatic architectural outdoor and indoor planning and design are numerous:

+ the siting and orientation of homes and buildings to optimize the use of solar, air, earth, and water energies.

+ a holistic perspective that weighs architecture, its networks, and the building process against ecologic factors.

+ making the microclimate of the site more gentle for outdoor and indoor space use.

+ responsive microclimatic design of the architecture should be in accord with air quality.

+ consideration of the ecologic context as well as relevance to architectural and neighboring conditions.

+ to optimize self-sufficiency of energy, *in situ* food production, and vitalization of the air, earth, natural ecosystems, and ourselves.

+ preservation of the existing microorganic vegetation and other ecologic factors by careful planning.

+ not using any power equipment for lawn care, landscaping, and cleaning walks and drives.

+ avoidance of air-polluting construction machines spewing toxic fumes and noise over the neighborhood.

+ creating outdoor micro-environ enclaves and spaces for pleasure, work, and play on days of little or no air pollution.

+ sensitive planning of indoor microclimatic clean air environs most suited to occupant activities and lifestyles.

+ to set up an indoor atmospheric retreat space for times of alert level outdoor air pollution.

+ removal of <u>all</u> odor-producing substances and items from the home.

+ outgassing all items of equipment, clothing, printed material, et al., before bringing them into the living area.

+ avoiding indoor air-polluting activities without adequate ventilation.

LANDSCAPING

The trees and other greenery of landscaping have a direct and constant connection with the oxygen and nitrogen of the air. Site-specific and neighboring landscaping has a filtration and climatological effect on air temperature and humidity and the vitalization of air for indoor and outdoor spaces.

Every variety of tree, bush, grass, or flowering plant has its specific effect upon the specific landforms and architecture of the site and adjoining sites. Trees, bushes, and plants can affect wind patterns, humidify, attenuate climatic extremes, and provide shade and negative ionization (needled varieties). By doing so, ventilation air and the indoor climate are notably benefited.

In dry climates water conservation and sustaining humidity can be accomplished with land contouring for water retention, compatible planting with moisture-retaining wood shavings or bark, and retention of roof water for irrigation. Care should be exercised not to plant trees or flowering plants that can exacerbate allergies or other respiratory conditions.

A hot sun and strong breeze can increase airborne allergens. Rain showers can clean the air but also increase the incidence of mold. At high altitude the least mold prevails. Sea air is most pollen free. Under moist outdoor conditions, a "mold shower" can occur on a breeze loaded with pollen. Olive, acacia, oak, and maple trees produce heavy pollen.

Lawns, trees, and bushes can provide localized oxygenation and absorption of carbon dioxide. *In situ* organic gardens can provide nutritional food without commercial pesticides and other air-polluting agricultural practices. The more that we landscape between and on the roofs of buildings, the more that we oxygenate the local atmosphere, absorb CO_2, and reduce the climatological impacts upon the architecture and its interiors.

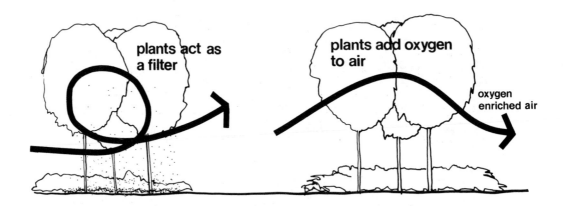

Choice of landscaping materials is important to reduce water demand and to provide climate- and pest-resistant plants that require the least maintenance and produce the best benefits for the site, architecture, and outdoor space use. Native plants and xeriscaping reduce irrigation demand, and usually native plants are more tolerant to changing conditions than imported varieties. Conserve water and maintenance with dense plantings of ground cover and spreaders as substantial landscape masses. This is also more aesthetically pleasing.

The microorganic complex of the soil should not be forgotten. Topsoil should be saved during construction or other earth disturbance avoided to preserve the ecologic soil balance. Landforming into berms and embankments controls wind movement and can effectively with planting reduce climatic impact upon outdoor spaces and the architecture, enhance privacy, and reduce noise.

Evergreen trees are most appropriate to attenuate cold northerly winter winds. Pinon pines, due to their bulk close to the ground and dense configuration of branches and needles, make excellent low-level windbreaks. Other evergreens such as Austrian pines slow down and turbulate wind. Located in the path of cold winter winds, they can act as a climatic buffer to the architecture. Deciduous trees that are selected for characteristics of shade can be placed to shade useful outdoor spaces and the architecture in summer. Deciduous trees that leaf out late in spring and lose leaves in early fall are especially desirable when using winter solar radiation. Be aware that bare wood and branches can decrease winter solar gains by as much as 10 to 15 percent.

A localized pollution occurs from the multifarious toxic chemicals and fertilizers used to keep lawns green and trees and plants "free" of insects and microorganic life that feeds upon or otherwise attacks them. The EPA has approved some of the less toxic chemicals. But caution is advised with all control methods, as well as in the use of appropriate biologic predators to control the microorganic and insect invaders.

Every blade of grass, plant, bush, and tree is a living organism supported by the nutrients of the soil, its microorganisms, and the oxygen and nitrogen of the atmosphere. With the loss of national and global forests, the more we can restore our worldly habitat with trees and other oxygen-giving, CO_2-absorbing vegetation, the more we can compensate for the declining sustainability of our continental and global oxygen supply.

Landforming and landscaping should be treated as critical and concordant parts of the architecture, our biologic and psycho-neural well-being, and Nature's ecosystemic integrity, vigor, and sustainability. The bottom line for site-specific existing or new architecture is sensitive landforming and landscaping in harmony with the sun, the atmosphere, natural ecosystems, and our own health and vitality.

INDOOR SPACES

Most of our lifetime is spent within the indoor spaces of homes, vehicles, and buildings. For most of us the only place where we can have a significant effect upon the air we breathe is in the home. Attention especially given to each room and space within a dwelling is an aid to evaluation and effectual decisions and procedures to secure cleaner and safer indoor air. Indoor spaces are usually designated for certain activities. Although a higher level of air quality is desirable for all indoor spaces, spaces where persons spend most of their time or use for sleeping or relaxing should be especially free of pollution.

Living and recreation rooms will be healthier places without a fireplace or stove. Bedrooms and children's play areas should be located away from sources of outdoor and indoor air pollution. A distinct source of airborne aggravation is the smoke from neighborhood fireplaces and stoves, which can make nocturnal ventilation a particular problem.

Kitchen ventilation should be adequate relative to what is being cooked and the type of fuel being used. Utility rooms are usually a repository and storage area for chemicals. Many substances used for cleaning and washing have allergenic and sometimes toxic properties. All chemicals are best stored away from living areas (such as in a ventilated garage or isolated storeroom). Highly toxic chemicals and combustible fluids should preferably be eliminated from the home. The choice should be for biologically safe, nontoxic substances.

Baths and restrooms can harbor harmful bacteria. Ventilation is essential. Vent-a-way toilets are a big boon for the direct elimination of excrement odors. But they are expensive and a low water demand flush is needed. Water, particularly showers, can liberate radon gas into the confines of the space. A city water supply is not likely to have, but well water has a higher probability of indoor radon emanation. Aeration and charcoal filtration can eliminate the radon hazard. Smoking is best relegated to the outdoors or to enclosed spaces specially isolated from other occupancy spaces and ventilated to the outside. Replacement air can come from other interior spaces that receive outside air or directly through a window or outside air intake. Recycling filtration of indoor air involves the cost of equipment and filter changes.

A significant portion of our time is spent in shopping, eating in restaurants, and attending affairs where people gather. Store environs in which either to work or shop leave much to be desired. Certain products and services have various degrees of odoriferous and often toxic outgassing and bioelectromagnetic fields counter to our body's neural and cellular functions.

The heady chemical odors of carpet showrooms, perfume counters, chemical fertilizer and other garden product stores, computer and other electronic equipment retailers (with their disturbing fields of electromagnetism), and a host of other retail and wholesale outlets can offend any sensitive nose or body. Clothing, luggage, and plastic items often contribute the disturbing odors. Some retail stores scent the air, which in itself can be a dilemma for persons with asthma and other respiratory dysfunctions. Most of what is made, printed, or otherwise assembled is anti-ecologic and anti-biologic.

As we might travel around and stay at hotels and motels, we can ask for no-smoking rooms. We can cautiously check a room before we move in as to other spray or chemical odors. Airports, bus stations, lobbies, restaurants, and other public gathering places present an ongoing dilemma. Even with nonsmoking sections, other pollutants or drifting smoke from a smoking area can be on a scale from annoying to overwhelming.

Hazardous substances and industrial processes have to meet OSHA and EPA standards and guidelines. Offices, retail stores, restaurants, and theaters have smoking regulations in some communities. Building codes have volumetric ventilation requirements, but seldom does indoor air have to conform to a quality standard. Ventilation controls that "sense" the air quality and adjust air flow accordingly are more energy efficient than constant ventilation air.

All indoor spaces, whether residential, commercial/industrial, or recreational, require ventilation to provide oxygen and remove carbon dioxide, as well as to remove airborne toxins and particulates. Slight negative pressure for ventilation by means of exhaust should prevail for all indoor occupant spaces subject to harmful levels of air pollution, except for sealed off basements and crawl spaces. When radon prevails, slight positive pressure is an advantage.

In general our daily exposure to air pollution and other harmful occurrences within the atmosphere depends upon <u>where</u> and for <u>how long</u> we spend most of our indoor and outdoor time. How we plan our time and place of activity affects our respiratory well-being and health. We can make our home a relatively <u>clean</u> and <u>safe</u> "air sanctuary" where we might spend as much of our time as possible.

SUNSPACES

Sunspaces can be a wonderful, practical, health-giving, and energy-saving part of a home. Well-designed preferably south or southeast sun rooms, sunspaces, solar atria, solar galleries, swimming pools, and attached greenhouses can add to life, pleasure, and well-being. Sunspaces can be primary or supplemental to indoor air quality, thermal effect, and day-lighting.

During the 1920s numerous homes were built with sun rooms. People often spent a considerable portion of their daytime hours within these spaces. Not only for homes, but sun rooms could also be a welcome asset for convalescent and nursing homes and for other institutional and commercial architecture such as eating, resting, recreational, and gathering places.

Depending upon climate and orientation, sunspaces can be appropriate for most parts of the continental U.S. They require very careful planning and design and sensitive respect for our psychoneural and biophysical responses. Daily and seasonal aspects of the sun, ventilation, and daylighting should balance with purpose and activity. Growing plants can help to vitalize and filter the air. Sunspaces can be good places for children's play and relaxation at any age.

Water of a pool, a fountain with spray, or waterfall that vitalizes the air with healthful negative ions or a lap pool for exercise can add to delight and vitality. Indoor pools are best located to accept direct passive solar gains as well as be heated by an active solar collection system. Pools may require transparent or other covers to avoid algal spores proliferation within the space.

Indoor sunspace radiant temperatures should be designed and controlled for comfort through all seasons. For the most part, sloping glass roofs are disadvantageous due to thermal losses to clear-sky temperatures, cold periods, overheating by direct solar radiation, accumulation of topside dust and dirt, and probabilities of rain and snow leakage. On the other hand, depending upon scale, location, interior planting (possibly with trees), and intended times and kinds of use, being able to see the sky elevates the spirits and adds a fascination and correspondence to the sky vault, clouds, stars, moon at night, and ever-changing climate with interludes of wind, snow, and rain. We are vitalized by what we see and feel as well as by what we breathe and eat.

Sunspaces can be designed as passive or hybrid solar cool and cold weather heating systems for the sunspace as well as for a home or building. Natural heat pump-type and inductive air flow convection and means of thermal retention and thermal lag can be used to warm and condition the interior of the architecture. Thermal mass and its direct solar radiation exposure, color, surface, and thermal retention properties are all germane to comfort and its extendibility during night and overcast hours. Brick, concrete, stone, water, and eutectic salts (phase-change materials) can effectively be used for direct or indirect retention of solar gains. Hybrid systems use fans or blowers with or without ductwork to convey the solar gains from a sunspace to other portions of the home or building (or into thermal storage) or to entire indoor spaces.

The author has used numerous hybrid as well as direct solar passive gain principles depending upon need and circumstance. Sunspaces can be open to or enclosed from other living areas. The advantage of closure combined with ability to open the sunspace is adaptability to time of day, use, and other circumstances of warmth, air convection, and air tempering.

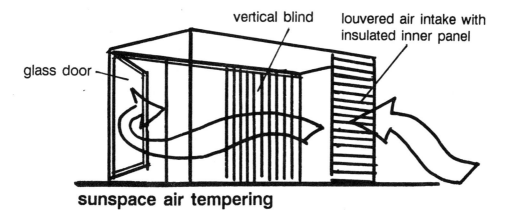

sunspace air tempering

dark solar-heat-transfer metal vertical blind tempers incoming outdoor cold air/reverse reflective side reflects solar radiation during warm and hot weather

A most salient feature of a sunspace is that it can be used to air-temper cool or cold outside air by solar gain before it is introduced into the interior architecture. Under-the-earth ducts (waterproofed earth-side heavy sheet metal plenums reinforced adequately against earth pressures, coated to resist rust when exposed to the moisture of the earth, and designed to avoid radon intrusion) can when connected to sunspaces (or to spaces within the architecture) earth-temper incoming ventilation air. They should be screened and designed for easy access for cleaning. They can be blower assisted or function on inductive air flows by temperature differential, stack and venturi action, and architectural design that aids ventilation by outdoor wind pressures.

Dark heat-absorbing vertical blinds placed within and to the rear of a sunspace will transfer direct solar gain to the air within the sunspace. Then by means of a thermostatically controlled blower the heated air can be expeditiously transferred from the sunspace into an inner thermal mass storage area or for heating interior space at some distance from the sunspace. A distinct advantage of this method over large thermal masses that receive direct solar radiation close to the exterior glazing (such as Trombe walls) is that reradiant and convective air losses can be greatly lessened by the rapid transfer of solar heat gain to interior space heating or thermal storage. Studies at the Solar Energy Research Institute indicate that as much as 50% of the solar energy received might be saved over direct gain thermal mass systems near the exterior glazing. Vertical (or horizontal) blinds or other solar-radiation-to-air-transfer devices can be devised to be heat absorbing for cold weather and highly reflective for summer reradiation through the exterior glazing. (See "Sunspace Design" in the Appendix.)

It should be noted that the heated air issuing by convection or other means from a greenhouse or sunspace will rise and stratify near the ceiling. Besides relocating or destratifying this stratified heated air by ductwork and blower, a ceiling fan or vortex floor fan (directed to the ceiling) can be used to conserve energy and increase comfort.

Sunspaces can be devised in all types of enclosure, size, form, fenestration, ventilation means, and thermal mass and be appointed and furnished in any appropriate manner relative to daily and seasonal space use. The design should require the least attention and manipulation for control over solar radiation, shading, daylighting, and ventilation.

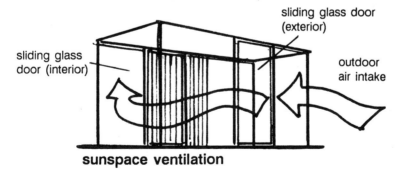

sunspace ventilation

outdoor air for indoor ventilation/screened outer patio door with inner patio door for control over ventilation/can also serve as a solar air tempering system or with plants to act as a greenhouse

71

Cross ventilation or inductive flow within the space and architecture should be a function of the sunspace. The type of glazing will have an influential effect upon the thermal effectiveness and visual and bodily comfort of the sunspace. The passage of daylight to the architectural interior and secondary thermal and air convection effects from sun room, atrium, gallery, greenhouse, or spa should not be neglected as a design consideration.

Complete integration of the site, architecture, interior usage, and visual and migrational relationships to usable exterior space is an effective resolution. Sun rooms, atriums, and other sunspaces can be designed for solar benefits, ventilation, comfort, and well-being and as an extension of the indoor living space as to treatment and character or be functionally and aesthetically designed with an outdoor ambience.

The ability to close off a sunspace with glazed doors, glass sections, or as may be a full or partial height thermal mass wall can provide a degree of daylighting, thermal transfer, and ventilation justifiable for the indoor living space. In particular when hot tubs, spas, and swimming pools might be within a sunspace or in another location, a separation from general indoor spaces is mandatory, in lieu of high airborne moisture, odors, and thermal considerations. The high humidity can be a problem within the space. Pool covers that allow penetration of direct solar radiation into the water are recommended for their reduction of surface evaporation as well as contribution to thermal gains within the pool. Matte finish dark to medium color ceramic tile over a concrete floor will act as a warm solar energy retaining mass in the pool area.

Solar atriums for some years have been popular for business and institutional buildings. Often with lofty height they become an indoor artificial sky. Full-sized trees within such spaces are not uncommon. They often act as a foyer or entry space to a building. Atriums of lesser scale for home or small business can be court-like penetrations anywhere within the architecture. Daylighting and direct solar radiation become assets by design. Their sky-related atmospheric quality can be a delight, but on the negative side, large heated skylighted areas can waste much energy as the upper warmest air is lost to outdoor cold and clear-sky temperatures.

A much better solution is the use of clerestories for daylight and concentration of direct and peripheral indoor solar gains. By centralizing natural air convection, all of the solar convective gains and the internal heat loads of lighting, people, processes, and equipment at the highest point of a solar gallery can be most effectively destratified by ceiling fans or relocated most advantageously by a photovoltaic powered blower to thermal storage or for space use. In warm and hot weather the centralized heat can be used to increase inductive ventilation by means of venturi or wind turbine roof venting.

Solar chimneys (west-facing vertical solar stacks in particular with thermal retention) can assist inductive indoor ventilation and thermal cooling. Screened intake air vents can most effectively cross-ventilate sunspaces and other indoor spaces when located close to the floor (operable panels should be insulated and gasketed) so as to achieve the desired amount of incoming outdoor air flow in combination with high stack action, roof venturi, or wind turbine exhaust. It should be noted that ventilation by means of operable windows is usually not ideal. The placement of windows for daylight, light control, and view is seldom as effective as operable intake air vents located for maximum ventilation and cooling effectiveness. The ASHRAE *Handbook of Fundamentals*, Chapter 22, in the "Ventilation and Infiltration" section under "Natural Ventilation" has equations used to calculate natural inductive ventilation that can be equated to air changes per hour (ACH).

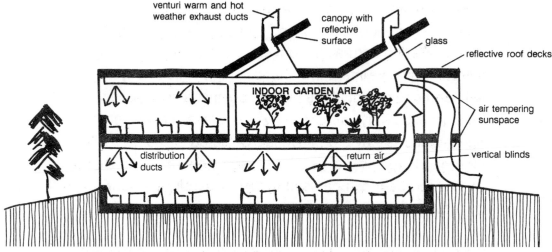

This small business or commercial building is shown with an indoor garden area that acts as an air tempering, CO_2-absorption, oxygenation, solar heating, solar inductive cooling, and ventilating element of the building.

Extensively planted enclosed solar roof gardens, atriums, or greenhouses can act as filtration, oxygenation, humidification, and air tempering thermal systems for homes and buildings. Whereas roofs generally only shed water from rain and snow, precipitation can be captured on the roof and be used internally to irrigate plants and trees. Enclosed solar roof gardens could be a delightful and useful space for a meeting, more extensive gatherings, or a place to eat, take a stroll, or exercise and enjoy physiologic and psychologic renewal.

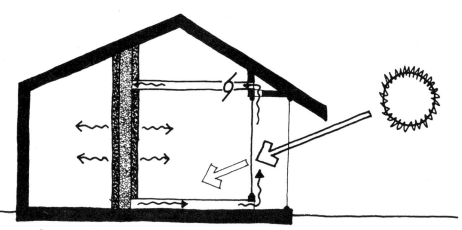

solar entrapment with dark heat-absorbing glazing/storage in vertical central thermal mass/secondary thermal gains

PART FOUR - INDOOR AIR RISKS

RADON

Radon-222 (an inert, odorless, radioactive gas) is a radioactive decay product of Radium-226 (member of the Uranium-238 decay chain). The half-life of radon is 3.8 days. The progeny (radon "daughters") from the decay of radon are ions that attach not only to the particulates of cigarette smoke, but also to dust particles and natural aerosols present in the air and to surfaces. When inhaled, some of the radioactive particles can lodge in the thorax and bronchial passageways of our respiratory system. In smokers they produce "hot spots" of radioactivity that can lead to lung cancer at such sites.

 - Radon Progeny

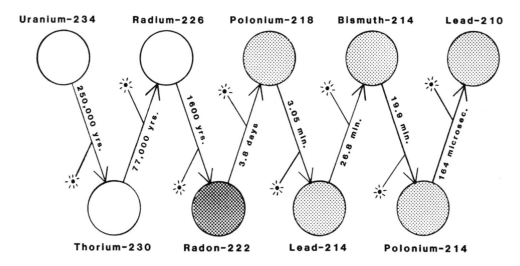

Radon in soils is common throughout the United States, with somewhat greater concentrations within granitic bedrock formations. At an 18-inch depth below the soil it averages about 100 picocuries per liter (pCi/l). A picocurie is a minute fraction (10^{-12}) of a Curie, a commonly used measure of radioactivity. One pCi/l represents the decay of about two radon atoms per minute in a quart of air. At a depth of 8 to 10 feet the pCi/l level tends to stabilize at 10 to 50 times greater concentration. The average outdoor level of radon in continental surface air is 0.2 pCi/l.

Many homes and buildings exhibit the presence of indoor radon. Radon gas emanates from radium in soils. Basements, crawl spaces, open earth areas, and the water supply (especially from wells) can introduce radon into interior spaces. The harm associated with water is not from drinking, but the release of radon into the air from activities that agitate or spray heated water (showering, dishwashers, etc.). A rough rule of thumb is that 10,000 pCi/l of radon in the water supply can produce 1 pCi/l of radon in indoor air. The harm from radon daughters comes largely from respiratory inhalation or from gamma radiation that results from their attachment to indoor and bodily surfaces. Gamma rays cause genetic effects and leukemia by photon interactions with germ cells of the body.

Radon can be detected by the alpha particle track-etch method that measures radioactive alpha particles, using detectors with a sensitized plastic strip placed at an 18-inch depth in the soil or judiciously located in indoor spaces of suspected high radon concentration (including the water supply). Low-priced canisters filled with activated charcoal granules for radon absorption are popular but often unreliable because collection by activated charcoal is very sensitive to fluctuations in temperature and humidity. Short-term radon testing can produce misleading results. Radon levels fluctuate widely over time, even hour to hour, due to variables such as changes in barometric pressure, outdoor winds moving around a structure that affect interior pressurization, and the amount of indoor ventilation. These variables make it difficult to get a true picture of radon concentrations.

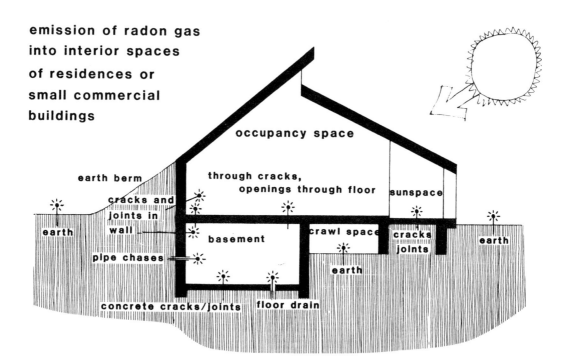

emission of radon gas into interior spaces of residences or small commercial buildings

Long-term monitor testing (for periods of at least two months) gives the most accurate evaluation. But if short-term testing is necessary, such as when a home is being sold, alpha-track detectors produce greater accuracy than activated charcoal detection kits. Electronic units are available that continuously monitor radon concentrations and give immediate short- or long-term digital readouts. Many private firms now offer radon testing and mitigation services. Some are highly reputable, others are not. "Let the buyer beware" is the watchword when engaging the services of these firms.

The principal means of radon control are by creating barriers to its influx into occupied spaces, by ventilating an air plenum space that intervenes between the radon source and occupied space, or when concentrations of radon within occupied spaces are low enough, to ventilate adequately to reduce the level of concentration.

The EPA recommends corrective action be taken when radon levels exceed 4 pCi/l. The American Society of Heating, Refrigerating and Air-Conditioning Engineers (ASHRAE) concurs that remedial efforts should be employed when radon levels exceed 4 pCi/l. The cleaner that we are able to make our indoor environment to reduce or eliminate smoking, dust, and other small airborne particulates, the less will be our danger from indoor radon progeny.

In tests performed in 1984 by the Harvard School of Public Health, negative ionization reduced radon progeny levels to 16 percent, and even lower with a fan for internal air circulation, to a level of 8 percent, as compared to pre-ionization levels. However, as we reduce the radon progeny attachment to particles in the air by negative ionization or other methods, more radioactive progeny ions and particles can concentrate on surfaces of the architectural and furnished interior and on body surfaces, sending harmful gamma radiation through our bodies as well as more alpha and beta radiation on skin surfaces.

The prescription is to tightly seal all cracks in basement concrete floors or walls (with a nonhardening caulking material), seal off interior earth-exposed surfaces, keep concrete surfaces dry (radon gas will transport through wet concrete), and seal off basement sumps and all other penetrations of basement slabs. Tightly seal around all foundation pipe chases and use seal-activated floor drains.

Ventilation under a concrete basement slab through a gravel bed or through a crawl space tightly sealed off from occupant spaces above is advisable. Ventilation of basement spaces is a primary protective measure. The question is how to ventilate during cold weather and minimize heat loss. Air-to-air heat exchangers that create an energy-conserving exchange between incoming outdoor air and outgoing indoor air at 60 to 80 percent efficiency will increase radon removal from buildings with limited interior air volumes and within economic determination. The air-to-air heat exchanger could be used to ventilate just the basement (allowing use of a smaller exchanger) or the whole house. Air-to-air heat pumps and conventional mechanical systems can provide an outdoor ventilation of indoor space where economics dictate for year-round heating, ventilating, and cooling. Sunspaces, solar greenhouses, and atriums can be economically and practically used for air tempering outdoor air for cold weather indoor ventilation.

The radon exhalation rate from the soil is relatively slow. Its rate of influx depends primarily upon negative pressure due to a drop in barometric pressure (modified by wind blowing over the architectural envelope and by soil moisture levels), stack action within the home or building, temperature differentials, or the use of combustion appliances, clothes dryers, or exhaust fans that draw air out of a building.

In a radon concentration study performed by R.L. Fleischer in New York, the living areas of energy-efficient homes without solar heat-storage masses had median radon concentrations that were 1.6 times those for conventional homes, and the energy-efficient homes with heat-storage masses had 5 to 6 times the radon of conventional homes.

For a basement or crawl space, there is no question that where the radon concentrations are high, direct mechanical ventilation of tubes, plenum space, or gravel bed under an impervious gas-protective cover or sealed concrete slab that is exhausted to the outside (not near an outside window) is a preferred remedy.

The National Concrete Masonry Association has issued a report on radon in buildings that describes several radon control measures in addition to those mentioned above. They point out that cracks in concrete floor slabs due to shrinkage can be reduced by avoiding the use of high slump concrete and by placing reinforcing mesh at the midpoint thickness of the slab. Infiltration of radon gas into the interior by diffusion through porous concrete materials can be completely eliminated through the use of various coatings. Research testing has shown that a 1/2" parge (plaster) coat would be effective in eliminating radon diffusion through foundation walls. Two coats of latex paint applied to one surface can reduce infiltration up to 50 percent; using fillers can increase this reduction up to 75 percent. Epoxy paint can also be used to seal interior masonry walls. Diffusion of radon gas through the floor slab can be eliminated by placing a 24-mil plastic barrier directly beneath the slab (sealed against gas release).

New studies at the New Mexico Institute of Mining and Technology reveal that radon is about 100 times more likely to bind to masonite, clay, and certain wood-based building materials than to quartz sand, fired brick, cinder block, or sheetrock (gypsum board). The research also found that the higher the moisture content or temperature of a given material, the less likely radon will adhere to it. This has implications for the design of radon barriers. Manufacturers may need to tailor the choice and thickness of materials to the average ambient temperature and humidity in the environment where they will be used.

For ventilated removal of radon under basement, main level, or other slab-on-grade concrete floor systems, a porous sub-slab radon control matting is available. It consists of a thick matrix of nylon filaments point-bonded to a polyester filter fabric. An air space is created between the slab and the subsoil. Radon gas can then be evacuated through ventilation tubes to the exterior.

The Masonry Association describes successful sub-slab ventilation methods (which depressurize the space beneath the slab) that consist of 4-inch perforated pipe embedded in crushed stone under the slab and running around the inside of the footing. A vertical 4-inch PVC standpipe with a 100 cfm exhaust fan is vented to the outside above grade. Basement sumps can be closed off and vented in a similar manner. *Solar Age* magazine reports that as an alternative (if crushed stone is not present under the slab) 3-feet square by 1-1/2 feet deep vented holes should be excavated in the sub-slab earth. The number of holes needed will vary with the permeability of the soil, with denser, less permeable soils requiring more holes. For relatively permeable soil, the recommendation is one hole for every 300-500 square feet.

Instead of a powered exhaust system for under-slab ventilation, passive ventilation could be used that relies on a roof-mounted turbine or tall stack for radon gas removal. However, with this system the ventilation rate will vary with the wind speed and changing temperatures. Another solution mentioned is increased natural ventilation of a basement or crawl space, with the caveat that windows or ventilators should be placed on both the windward and leeward sides to prevent creating a negative pressure.

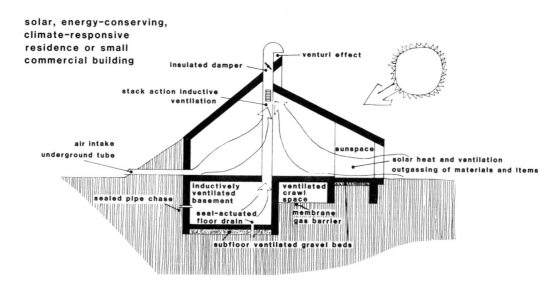

radon control strategies

For new construction, the *Solar Age* report gives several additional radon-prevention guidelines. Concrete and block foundation walls should be reinforced to minimize cracks. The tops of hollow core block walls should be sealed with an ethafoam sill sealer and butyl caulk. For slabs-on-grade and basement slabs, the number of joints should be minimized and perimeter control joints should be caulked with polyurethane. Sub-slab drainage systems should have 4 inches of crushed stone and interior footer drains (in addition to exterior drains) so that sub-slab ventilation can be readily added if needed.

To reduce radon concentrations in water, the most common technique is to install an activated carbon filter in the water supply line. The filter will adsorb radon long enough for it to decay. However, gamma radiation from the decay products trapped in the filter bed can exceed safety standards. Radioactive buildup in the filter may also cause disposal problems. Aeration systems are also available to reduce radon levels in water.

Other precautions: Determine the risk of any site with suspected high levels of radioactivity. Any well drilled on such property should also be tested. Even if the property does not have a high level of radioactivity, any home or building placed on the site should be designed and built for effective control over radon. The Environmental Protection Agency has available guidelines that address radon reduction in new construction. Additionally, there are now companies that specialize in selling radon-mitigation products, including prepackaged radon ventilation systems, fans, caulk, sealants, and other materials. (See reference section)

Many people live in or spend time in garden levels, basements, or partial basements of homes and apartments. Some people live in underground houses. Ventilation is a primary reductive means after sealing all cracks and applying other methods to stop an influx of radon and to safeguard occupant well-being.

When existing conditions do not allow for good (preferably cross) ventilation, simple to more ingenious means can be employed. Prevailing seasonal wind patterns, solar orientation that can aid inductive ventilation and air tempering, earth air tempering, topography, and vegetation have an effect on natural ventilation. For radon gas removal, natural ventilation should be an *a priori* consideration when test levels do not exceed 4 pCi/l.

However, if higher levels of radon prevail after intervention and other mitigation strategies have been employed, somewhat pressurizing the indoor space with an outside air intake blower fan with an outlet on the lee side or using an air-to-air indoor positive pressure heat exchanger may prove to adequately lower radon concentrations. Exhaust fans in kitchens, baths, or elsewhere in use will tend to increase radon emanation from the soil unless the emissions are tightly sealed off. The fans will exhaust radon but create a negative pressure over the soil. Every project has its idiosyncracies. If radon persists at unacceptable test levels, professional assistance should be sought.

Simple strategies such as adding another window, an outside air vent, or cutting in a louvered door or patio door when possible to outdoor grade levels can in times of moderate outdoor temperatures add to ventilation and radon removal. However, during periods too cold or hot for bringing in very much outdoor air, some means is needed for air tempering. Either solar, earth, or mechanical air tempering can then be used to condition incoming outdoor air for indoor comfort.

A garden level or basement infers that there are likely to be one or more stories above. A responsibility in venting radon out of a lower level should be to do so to prevent capture by windows or vents of an upper level. A strategy that can be used is to have lower vents located considerably out of line with upper windows or to carry ducts up through the roof with a weather-protection roof cap. The stack action of ductwork can serve for garden level or basement ventilation when carefully located to optimize indoor air flow, but the negative soil pressure with radon is likely to increase. To advantage both ventilation and radon control, outside air can be forced in mechanically, preferably through a sunspace built to act as an air tempering and passive solar heating system.

As may be possible for an existing condition of architecture and site (and budgetwise acceptable), a south, east, or less desirable west excavation at grade or at basement level can be made so that a sunspace can be designed and built to act for passive solar collection and useable space. Any number of variations can be made on this theme. An ideal arrangement can be planned (as the site space may allow) for a terrace patio to the south in front of the sunspace that will benefit from solar exposure, provide an outdoor space at grade, and relieve the stigma of a garden- or basement-level space. Ventilation with outdoor air can be accomplished by low ventilation (as close to the ground as possible) or with a louvered door, with a solid insulated door closing over it to control incoming air at the end of the space. Any outdoor areas with a cut grade should be properly drained.

In any case, the first issue should be the certainty of being able to control radon at a safe level before alterations, renovations, or additions are initiated. In the planning of garden-level or basement spaces for occupancy, radon control strategies should be aptly applied to ensure safe conditions for occupancy.

SMOKING

Smoking is a principal offender of indoor air quality. Tobacco smoke contains more than 3,000 constituents, many of which are toxic, carcinogenic, tumorigenic, or have adverse radioactive affinities and properties. Smoking one cigarette raises indoor air concentrations of submicron particles 10 to 100 times.

Radon progeny (from decay of radon gas) attach to the smaller particulates of tobacco smoke. Tobacco smoke particles are in the .01 to 4.0 micron range. Radon decay products attached to airborne tobacco-smoke particles deposit in the bronchi where they emit carcinogenic alpha radiation. Radon decay products will also attach to hair and similar natural and synthetic fibers. They concentrate by ion deposition on the tips of hairy surfaces. Dr. Edward Martell at the National Center for Atmospheric Research states that airborne radon progeny (plus radioactivity in tobacco) are the probable agents of cancer and atherosclerosis.

Other tobacco smoke constituents include carbon monoxide (a toxic agent) and tarry particulates that contaminate hair, body surfaces, clothing, and all indoor surfaces. Not only is tobacco smoke a major indoor pollutant, but it greatly escalates maintenance costs and increases burn and fire damage. Smoker and nonsmoker alike are affected by the direct and secondhand tobacco smoke emissions.

The most effective control is prohibition of indoor smoking with specified enclosed areas designated for smokers. Smokers should be segregated into interior architectural spaces that are separately exhausted in a manner adequate to meet projected concentrations of tobacco smoke. Whereas air changes per hour in the home or nonsmoking work environment may be from 0.5 to 4, the air changes for smoking places should be 12 to 60 or more.

Separate outdoor intake air is preferable for interior smoking room enclosures. Such intake air will have to be tempered by heating and cooling means relative to seasonal temperature change. Some energy conservation can occur through thermal exchange between the incoming and outgoing (exhaust) airstreams. Means of accomplishing this include heat wheels, heat pipe transfer, air-to-air heat exchangers, and other heating and cooling mechanisms. Only by the limitation of smoking to definitive, separate, completely enclosed rooms, lounges, and spaces can indoor air quality be reasonably addressed. Doors to smoking areas should be kept closed, and adjoining areas should have positive air pressure to avoid intrusion of smoky air when a door may be opened for access.

Other means to control indoor smoke can alleviate to a lesser degree the intrusion of cigarette and other tobacco smoke upon everyone within range. Certain gaseous effluents of cigarette smoke are heavier than air. The dispersion and direction of smoke should be given particular planning and design attention. In all cases, nonsmokers should be placed in the path of incoming outdoor air (even when such air is polluted, it is far less likely to be a risk than the tobacco smoke) and the smokers located downstream from indoor ventilation or on the negative air pressure side of indoor space.

The best filtration systems, including electrostatic/charcoal air cleaners, negative ionizers, and magnetic field devices, will to a degree reduce the contaminating particulates and injurious tobacco fumes, but filters require short-term constant maintenance to be effective. Also, until the interior air makes one or more passes (more usually needed) through the filtration systems, some of the air on its way to the return remains polluted until refiltered again and again.

To reduce the effects of cigarette and other tobacco smoke, maximum natural ventilation or high levels of mechanical ventilation are required. Localized removal or filtration of tobacco smoke, particularly before it contaminates ducts and air handling systems, is preferable to depending only on centralized systems to handle the problem.

All types of air-cleaning devices and machines discussed within this book will in some degree remove cigarette and other tobacco smoke from the air. Some manufacturers claim over 90 percent removal within laboratory tests. In actual conditions of heavy continual smoking, and depending upon the number of smokers in a given room volume, ventilation rate, and other factors, a much lower percentage of removal is likely. With activated charcoal and other adsorption filters, gaseous elements of the smoke will be partly removed, but particulate filters will have no effect on these elements.

As air-cleaning devices and machines may be employed where smokers and nonsmokers work or gather, do not expect adequate relief from the effect of smoking upon the nonsmoker. There is no equivalent for the complete elimination of smoking from indoor spaces.

No-smoking signs are inexpensive. Air-cleaning machines and filter changes can be relatively expensive. They can also not be adequately effective. Negative ionizing devices can leave unsightly and frustrating dark residues on ceilings and walls as smoke particulates "ground off" on these surfaces. Only cleaning with repainting is likely to cover the soilage.

The Environmental Protection Agency has recently released a position paper on smoking. It indicts environmental tobacco smoke (ETS) as one of the most widespread and most harmful indoor air pollutants, for which there is no safe level of exposure. The EPA states that ETS causes lung cancer and heart disease and that segregation and separate ventilation will reduce ETS concentrations but not adequately protect nonsmokers in an airspace with typical ventilation. To quote from the report:

95

"The most effective way to minimize exposure is to restrict smoking to areas that are <u>separately</u> ventilated and <u>directly</u> exhausted to the outside or by eliminating smoking in the building entirely." (emphasis added)

Businesses would do best by hiring nonsmokers. Smokers cost everyone (including themselves) extra cleaning of hair and clothes, extra maintenance of indoor surfaces from sticky residues and burns, and interference with business performance when their addicted demand causes them to light up.

More and more municipalities are limiting where and under what conditions smoking is permissible. Laws that prohibit smoking in every public gathering place but provide a properly ventilated smoker's lounge or room with independent air systems separately partitioned from all other spaces are urgently needed, particularly in our age of energy-conscious "tight" buildings.

Only when smokers might bear the full responsibility and direct and indirect costs for their unfortunate habit, and smoking is considered to be entirely unacceptable in places where nonsmokers are, can substantive elimination of this principal offending element of indoor air quality be achieved. About 70 percent of our adult population does not smoke. Polls have indicated that 87 percent of all adults -- smokers and nonsmokers alike -- now believe companies should either ban smoking at work totally or should restrict it to designated areas, and 75 percent of Americans believe that smokers should not light up in the presence of nonsmokers.

The higher risk of lung cancer in passive smokers compared to other nonsmokers may be attributed to several factors: exposure to higher indoor radon progeny levels, inhalation of radon progeny attached to airborne smoke particles of relatively large size, and the slower rate of clearance for smoke tar particles and attached radon progeny at deposition sites in the lungs.

> *-- Dr. Edward A. Martell, in **Proceedings of the 3rd International Conference on Indoor Air Quality and Climate**, 1984*

Smoking that for years was condoned in the workplace, public places, and at social gatherings is now condemned as a health hazard to all persons exposed to it within indoor space. Legislative measures at state and national levels are needed to prohibit smoking in all public and private places where people gather indoors, such as public and private institutional buildings, indoor recreation areas, theaters, stores, food markets, offices, and restaurants.

Legislation at the national level is essential to stop all direct or indirect tobacco subsidies, to prohibit all tobacco product advertising and promotion, and most of all, to outlaw all cigarette vending machines that give children of any age direct access to cigarettes.

Over 400,000 persons die each year from the effects of smoking. Women and youth remain the principal targets of the cigarette industry. The addictive power of the cigarette is greater than that of heroin.

AIRBORNE PARTICLES

Indoor air is usually laden with fine particles. They originate from natural and synthetic sources. The pollen, particles, and dust contained in outdoor air are introduced into home and building interiors by ventilation. There are no single-pass filters that can completely eliminate such potential allergens and irritants, but by using a powered intake air blower with high-efficiency filters, they can be reduced. In cold or hot weather air tempering will be required. In climates where the summertime temperatures are cooler at night, such an outdoor air pressurizing system can provide effective nocturnal cooling. With this filtered and pressurized system, windows or vents should be opened appropriately for the escape of air and to provide cooling in spaces where it is most desired.

Smoking, cooking, fire burning, and various processes and activities of home and industry generate particulates in indoor air. Particulates, including their possible gaseous accompaniments, require filtration appropriate to their size and characteristics. Size is determined in microns (millionths of a meter).

Interception filters work by sieving out particles that will not pass through them and by adherence to webs of filter fibers. Particles that adhere to filters of this type, to a degree until the filter is too clogged, intercept incoming particles, improving their efficiency. Clogged filters of mechanical systems, however, can seriously affect heating and cooling efficiency and impair adequate air flow for effective filtration. HEPA filters are especially effective in capturing smaller submicron particles but require proportionately greater blower capacity due to their greater resistance to the passage of air.

Aero-allergens are particulates of natural and synthetic origin capable of producing an allergic reaction when present in the atmosphere. These include pollen, spores, dust, mites, animal dander, and certain kinds of stuffing materials such as feathers, kapok, and cottonseed. These aero-allergens can cause allergic asthma and allergic rhinitis (nasal irritation). Dust, as a particulate, can present particular problems, since it can be an irritant, an aero-allergen, or serve as a transport system for other allergens (including all of the substances mentioned above).

Dust mites flourish in carpeting, bedding, and upholstered furniture. They like a warm, humid environment and live on flakes of skin shed by people. The feces of these microscopic creatures are a notable source of allergic reactions.

Fungi that produce spores can be found indoors and out-doors, mainly in the forms of mold, dry rot, and mildew. Indoor sources of fungi can be any place or object where moist conditions exist, such as vaporizers, humidifiers, central air conditioning systems, houseplants, shower curtains and stalls, refrigerator drip trays, moist basements, and areas where water seepage may occur that creates moist materials.

(Note: Popular ultrasonic humidifiers, when used with tap water, can produce exceedingly high concentrations of fine mineral particles in the air. These units should only be used with distilled or demineralized water.)

Because mold grows with persistence under moist conditions, dryness should be maintained. Chlorinated mold removal products are available, but nontoxic inhibitors offer more protection for persons sensitive and reactive to mold. In general, care exercised to prevent outdoor dust and other aero-allergens from entering indoor space is a judicious precaution. Outdoor trees, plants, weeds, leaves, or other conditions that breed spores or exude pollens that cause distress should be removed, or affected persons might move further from the source. These particulates can be reduced to some extent in incoming air with a self-activated electrostatic generating filter. Meticulous and as often as appropriate cleaning of all indoor spaces with nontoxic means that "raise the least dust" should be routine. Central vacuum systems are advocated for sensitive individuals.

A number-one consideration is to design and furnish interiors without dust-catching moldings and details. Choose materials and surfaces that are easy to clean. Avoid draperies; use vertical blinds that collect the least dust. Or where privacy and solar control are not issues, choose no blinds or draperies at all. Use fabrics that do not shed. Do not use any harmful sprays.

Respirable particles can reach astounding concentrations indoors, particularly where there is smoking going on.

*-- Stephen Budiansky in **Environmental Science and Technology**, Sept. 1980*

Asbestos

Until banned by the Environmental Protection Agency (EPA) in 1978, sprayed-on asbestos was pervasively used as a fire shield in the steel structure of buildings, as well as for acoustical ceilings and as a component of resilient floor coverings. Asbestos appeared in fire-protective clothing and for a host of other uses.

Its fibers can cause lung disease. The prevalence of asbestos has caused particular concern either in its removal or in intervening to prevent its mineral fibers from entering the indoor atmosphere. Strategies and techniques for removal and containment have been developed that meet EPA guidelines. No asbestos removal or containment work should be done without strict adherence to government regulations. Companies experienced and skilled in dealing with asbestos should be employed for any remedial work.

On an international basis, Canada is mining, promoting, and exporting large quantities of asbestos. Asbestos does have an incontestable value for its exceptional fire-proofing attributes. Significant shipments are still being made by Canada into the U.S. Caution is advised where asbestos might be present in existing buildings and also where it may appear in any product.

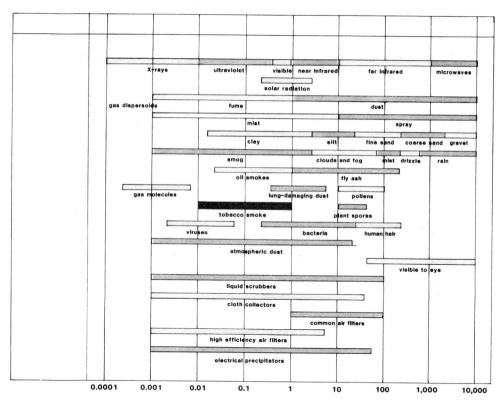

Particle Diameter in Microns

INDOOR COMBUSTION

In addition to smoking and coal or wood-burning fireplaces and stoves, other indoor combustion sources can release large amounts of pollutants into the indoor air. These include gas-fired appliances such as ranges, clothes dryers, water heaters, and furnaces; unvented gas- and kerosene-fired space heaters; oil-fired furnaces; and oil and kerosene lamps. Nitrogen dioxide, carbon monoxide, nitrous oxides, sulfur oxides, hydrogen cyanide, hydrocarbons, formaldehyde, and particulates are some of the pollutants produced by these devices. Toxic effects of these contaminants include impaired cardiopulmonary function and increased respiratory infection.

Several measures can be taken to alleviate these problems. Unvented appliances should not be used in any situation. Residential gas ranges can have pilotless ignition systems and should be equipped with a range hood that vents to the outdoors, with a fan capable of 140 cubic feet per minute (cfm) of flow (according to Lawrence Berkeley Lab tests). Restaurant kitchens and commercial applications require far greater flow rates for exhaust hoods. Electric ranges are preferred for new construction or when replacing an old unit.

High-efficiency furnaces with sealed combustion units are best, which vent exhaust gases to the outside and draw in outdoor combustion air through a totally closed system. Such equipment is currently available. These units use combustion air independent from the rest of the indoor air, eliminating the potentially lethal occurrence of chimney backdrafting in tight homes and buildings and reducing infiltration. Similar systems for water heaters are also on the market. Electronic ignition instead of a constantly burning gas pilot conserves energy.

It should be noted that even a vented combustion appliance, if poorly maintained, damaged, or faulty (such as a furnace with a cracked heat exchanger), can be a significant threat to indoor air quality.

Natural gas and propane are both toxic and can be lethal. All precautions should be taken to avoid gas pipe leakage in indoor spaces. Joints and welds in pipes should not occur under concrete slabs. The piping should be continuous to the point of use for inspection with all joints and welds accessible. Safety cut-off valves activated by any gas leak should be located at the equipment, particularly gas-fired furnaces, boilers, and hot water heaters that are visually remote. The venting of all gas, liquid, or solid fuel equipment should follow manufacturer's instructions and meet all regulatory codes.

COMBUSTION AIR

Gas-fired furnaces, boilers, hot water tanks, and other equipment including gas ranges require combustion air. The product of combustion is carbon dioxide. It is the same gas we exhale in the respiration process. All of these devices deplete the indoor air of oxygen. Oxygen-consuming processes and equipment compete with our essential respiratory need for oxygen.

Devices and equipment of any type that function on the basis of combustion should not be used in unvented spaces. Deprivation of oxygen, exposure to toxic gases of combustion, and danger of fire are attendant risks.

In older homes combustion air is often taken from indoor basement air or from living spaces. In such cases the replacement of gas- or oil-fired space heating equipment with new high-efficiency furnaces or boilers (80% or more efficient vs. less than 50%) with a direct supply of outside air, as the envelope of the older home is made "tight" by caulking or otherwise sealing the home from outdoor air infiltration, has multiple benefits. Utility bills should be accordingly less, indoor oxygen would not be depleted, and fire safety is likely to be improved.

Heating equipment tends to be starved for oxygen. As persons tighten their homes for energy conservation, the combustion needs for both space heating and domestic hot water heating, gas-heated clothes dryers, or other items should be considered. Natural gas, propane, and other gases or volatile fuels should be treated with respect and caution. Particular risk attends health and property in the storage and use of any fuels or combustible fluids that vaporize.

It is best that gas- or oil-fired heating units be relocated from garages or from the main or basement living areas of the dwelling for safety and health. The best arrangement for new construction is for units (space heating or domestic hot water) to be installed in separate fire-rated enclosures in the attic, basement, or other places with direct outside combustion air and venting provided. They must be absolutely isolated by an "airtight" separation from all living areas and with an exterior or gasketed tight-fitting interior access door. The more centralized the location, the easier effective distribution can be accomplished.

With regard to new or older commercial buildings, each case needs to be specifically evaluated or reevaluated as to intent, conditions, efficiency, economics, and building code requirements.

THERMAL SYSTEMS

The site, the architecture, and its interior by <u>holistic ecologic integrated design</u> should be <u>the system</u> for thermal comfort, health, and vitality of the occupants. In the interest of ecologic sustainability, energy conservation, and self-sufficiency, either no or the least demand on gas and electric utilities should be the prime objective for new or older homes and buildings. To design or redesign for optimal site-specific sun, earth, air, and water energies has the greatest advantages. The outdoor atmosphere is significantly spared from pollution and denigration at the utility source and at the site of the architecture.

The most favorable ecologic and economic local and global resolution is when either no or minor mechanical assistance is provided for the most effectual use of solar, air, earth, and water energies. Photovoltaic panels can provide the electrical needs for natural and mechanical energy systems.

Think, plan, and design for the most effective interface between natural and mechanical systems. Depending upon climate, the design of the architecture, and the lifestyle of the occupants, natural systems should have priority over mechanical components.

Differentiation in the use of indoor spaces is best served and energy conserved by meeting <u>specific</u> thermal, ventilation, and daylighting needs. Rooms and other spaces of activity or rest

108

can with natural and mechanical control over the indoor atmosphere and the internal environs be in phase with occupant use. Air quality directly relates to the type, characteristics, and design of natural and mechanical systems.

Thermal comfort is best achieved with radiant heating. The radiant heat from a thermal mass, from solar radiation, or from a hydronic or electric system is of greater comfort and biologic benefit (when ventilation is provided by other means) than heat from a forced-air system. However, for homes and buildings that need mechanical air conditioning, greater economy is realized with the installation of a combined forced-air HVAC duct system.

High-efficiency gas-fired hydronic boilers with thermal-zoned piping to radiant baseboard, radiators, fin tubes recessed in floor or wall slots, fan-coil units, or in a radiant floor, wall, or ceiling installation can be designed to the specific requirements of indoor spaces. The author has favored these radiant applications along with boilers that combine or use a side-arm heat exchanger for domestic or commercial hot water heating. As a precaution against freezing during cold weather, glycol can be added to the system. Periodic checks should be made to assure the degree of freeze protection.

Because of economy, ease of installation and repair, and thermal zoning, radiant baseboard is often a system of choice. Large pieces of furniture that set on the floor against the baseboard, however, will act as a radiant and convective thermal barrier. Hot water system piping should be insulated in unheated areas, although uninsulated under-floor distribution can keep a basement and the floor above desirably warm. Due to a possible adverse effect upon leg muscles, the author has not used radiant floor systems except as a <u>secondary</u> source of indoor heat. Secondary refers to lower-temperature entire floor or full-temperature transient or perimeter floor areas where people do not spend time. Due to the gross waste of energy, outdoor radiant systems for heating driveways and sidewalks should not be used.

Forced-air systems with duct distribution to various rooms and spaces from a central gas-fired furnace and air conditioning unit are the predominant means for heating and cooling homes and small commercial buildings. Advantages are relatively low initial cost, high efficiency (with newer models), and vertical, downflow, upflow, horizontal, heat pump, and air filtering options. Disadvantages are noise, usually single zoning for a home or small commercial building, dust-accumulating ductwork, buildup of mold or other harmful microorganisms in ductwork, and regulating air movement so as not to be disturbing.

In office and retail applications outdoor air must be introduced to provide oxygenated ventilation air for the number of occupants present. In larger commercial and institutional installations, duct systems prevail to provide balanced flows of heating, air conditioning, and ventilation in accord with various levels of activity, changing external solar and climatic conditions, and internal loads from equipment, processes, lighting, and occupants.

Depending upon their coefficient of performance (COP), heat pumps as forced-air electric systems can save energy by extracting heat from the cooler temperatures of outdoor air. They are most applicable to homes and small commercial buildings. As outdoor temperatures drop below the threshold of the COP, the heat pump has to fall back upon direct electric resistance heating to meet the heat demand of the building.

Other forms of electric heating are radiant ceiling, radiant baseboard (not recommended as the red glowing heated resistance elements strip off negative ions from the air flow and have abrupt disturbing hot and cold cycles), and radiant hydronic baseboard. Radiant electric hydronic baseboard systems have the advantage of low initial cost, with thermostatically controlled temperatures tailored to specific rooms and interior spaces, and they lend well to the economy of a demand controller. Radiant electric ceiling installations heat people, floor, and objects with radiant energy. But they produce questionable electromagnetic fields. Most importantly, these systems do not contribute directly to indoor air pollution. Hot water electric boiler systems with baseboard distribution can perform with respective advantages and disadvantages of individual room electric hydronic systems but at a usually higher utility cost. In most areas electricity will be more expensive than natural gas.

111

In an optimal energy-conserving solar home or place of business where mechanical heating is supplemental rather than primary, the utility demand can be considerably reduced. "Clean" air at the site (while not at the polluting power plant) is a local gesture to air quality.

CHEMICALS

We live in a chemical world. There are approximately 65,000 chemicals used commercially in the United States and nearly 12,000 chemical manufacturing plants. A 1984 National Academy of Sciences report stated that no information is publicly available to determine whether or not 80 percent of these 65,000 chemicals pose a health hazard. The American Chemical Society registers 600,000 new chemicals a year, many of which become commonly used new products.

Toxic emissions and waste plague our local and global atmosphere. Chemistry that serves industry is too often an airborne threat to nearby populations. We are a chemical society. The clothes we wear, plastics, and other (likely to be) toxic materials, devices, and equipment put us at risk. The homes we live in and places where we work and play are loaded with diverse anti-biologic chemicals.

Chemicals that affect indoor air quality are those associated with architecture, the interior, and for maintenance. The more selective we are in the choice and specification of materials (chemical or otherwise), the more we can control indoor air quality.

Under the architectural aegis, plywood, particle board, and wood paneling that outgas formaldehyde should not be specified. Nonrisk materials may be substituted or such boards be coated to prevent the outgassing. Exterior grade plywood can be substituted for interior grade sheets. Using phenol resins instead of urea-formaldehyde resins, it is considered about 10 times less toxic. (New HUD standards for mobile homes are resulting in production of low-formaldehyde-emitting plywood, particle board, and other products that have even greater reduction of outgassing rates). Oil-based paints, finishes, and coatings as well as toxic solvents pose greater risk than most latex-based materials. During application and throughout the curing stage of paint and coatings, indoor spaces should be well ventilated and should be unoccupied. Adhesives and caulking used indoors should be specified as nontoxic (particularly for health facilities).

Carpets manufactured of chemically synthesized fibers can shed small particles into the indoor atmosphere and/or outgas harmful toxins from the fibers, the backing, or the pad under the carpet. The adhesives used to lay carpet and other floor coverings can be repulsive in odor as well as harmful to health. Floor coverings that contain benzyl chloride, toluene, or other harmful chemicals should be avoided as well as the toxic adhesives used to apply them. Wool carpeting can be substituted for synthetic brands (for those not sensitive to this natural fiber).

Synthetic-fabric-covered furniture and surfaces can exude both gaseous organic compounds and fibrous particulates. Natural fibers such as wool, cotton, and linen also shed particulates that can be allergenic to some persons.

114

Draperies, wall coverings (especially vinyl-coated wallpapers), newspapers, magazines, books, and polyurethane foam pillows, mattresses, and pads all give off chemical gases and particulates that tend in some measure to pollute the indoor air.

The most judicious procedure is to design the interior without the specification of materials that exude strong odors or are known (inquire) to contain chemicals of a harmful type.

Chemicals commonly used for cleaning, maintenance, and for other household and business purposes (including materials used by artists, artisans, mechanics, and others) should where possible be selected as nontoxic. Where they might be toxic, isolate them from general occupant spaces and greatly increase ventilation.

Some of the commonly used household products that are potential indoor pollutants include:

- + cleaning agents
- + mothballs
- + furniture and shoe polishes, waxes, petrochemical-based materials and solvents
- + chlorine bleach
- + insecticides, antifungicides, mold inhibitors
- + paint, varnish, paint stripper and thinner, turpentine, lacquers
- + aerosol sprays

+ art and hobby materials
+ room deodorizers, other deodorants
+ nail polish and nail-polish remover
+ lighter fluid, charcoal fire starter

Pesticides used for wood-boring insect control, such as chlordane and heptachlor, can be a particular concern, as residual concentrations of these extremely toxic chemicals can contaminate indoor air and surfaces. Metal termite shields can be used in place of these chemicals.

Safe alternatives do exist to hazardous household chemicals. These alternatives can reduce the risk of exposure, are less harmful to the environment, and are often far less expensive than their toxic counterparts. Nearly all household cleaning tasks can be performed with the following products: baking soda, Borax, washing soda, vinegar, lemon juice, Murphy's Oil Soap, and Ivory soap.

The list below covers common household products known to contain toxic ingredients or that produce reactions in chemically sensitive individuals. Safe alternatives are given that are generally equally effective and often much less expensive than their commercial counterparts.

Product	Substitute or Alternate Method
ammonia-based cleaners	vinegar, salt, and water mixture; water and borax

116

abrasive cleaners (oven, drain)	1/2 lemon dipped in borax, then rinse
caustic cleaners (oven, drain)	oven cleaners: baking soda for scouring; drain cleaners: 1/2 cup salt or 1/4 cup baking soda with 1/4 cup vinegar, followed by boiling water
floor, furniture, shoe polishes	1 part lemon juice, 2 parts olive oil or vegetable oil; 1 tbsp. Carnauba wax (melted) into 2 cups mineral oil. Avoid shoe polishes with methylene chloride, trichloroethylene, or nitrobenzene.
silver polishes	soak in boiling water with baking soda, salt, a piece of aluminum; use toothpaste for small pieces
toilet bowl cleaners	paste of borax and lemon juice; baking soda and toilet brush
tub and tile cleaners	white vinegar; borax and water
disinfectants	1/2 cup borax in 1 gallon water - avoid phenol-based germicides
spot removers	club soda, cold water (blood stains), baking soda (animal urine), fuller's earth (grease spots);

	launder fabrics when possible to remove stains
mothballs	cedar chips, sachet of dried lavender, rosemary and mint, whole peppercorns; store woolens properly
rug/upholstery cleaners	sprinkle on dry cornstarch, then vacuum
enamel or oil-based paints and finishes	nontoxic paint technology, latex or water-based paints and finishes
house plant insecticide	spray on mixture of soap and water, rinse off
flea collars and sprays	gradually add brewer's yeast to pet's diet, use herbal repellents
roach and ant killers	roaches: mix of baking soda and powdered sugar; ants: chili powder, paprika, or red pepper to hinder entry
air fresheners	ventilation; baking soda; spice (such as ginger or nutmeg) sprinkled on floor, then vacuum; cloves and cinnamon added to boiling water, let simmer; herb sachets
window/glass cleaners	1 tbsp. vinegar in 1 quart water; rub with newspaper

chlorinated scouring powders	scouring powder that does not contain chlorine or talc (may be contaminated with asbestos); salt, borax, baking soda
rat/mouse killer	traps; mixture of plaster of Paris and flour with sweetener

Many garments are required to be dry-cleaned, which avoids probable damage by shrinking, fading, or other problems caused by washing. The most common dry-cleaning method uses perchlorethylene. Although this chemical solvent evaporates and outgasses in a short time from a garment, to be on the "safe side," the garment should be aired out away from occupied places within a home and not be hung directly in a clothes closet or bedroom. A well-ventilated room, a shady area in a sunspace, or hanging a short time outdoors on a porch in a sun- and weather-protected place (where no one will swipe the garment) can avoid the possibility of an adverse effect from lingering fumes. Damage to your body's neural system, cancer, and liver damage are possible by exposure to toxic dry-cleaning emissions.

The vast majority of products we buy have a damaging effect upon the global atmosphere. Packaging, handling, and waste are all part of the issue. A recent national survey of 1000 adults by the Michael Peters Group, an international design company, revealed that 89 percent of those contacted were concerned about the environmental impact of the products they purchased. Businesses have begun to seriously evaluate what they can do to decrease or eliminate adverse effects of their processes and products upon the atmosphere and environment.

SPRAYING AND CHLOROFLUORO-CARBONS

Spraying our outdoor and indoor atmosphere with a wide variety of aerosol products is a national preoccupation. Every substance, from medications to pesticides, is duly sprayed. There is no more singular way in which to charge the air with respirable particles and chemicals than a spray can or other spray devices (except, perhaps, smoking). Many of the particulates from spraying fall out within a relatively short time, but toxicity and irritants are often inherent in both what is being sprayed (usually a chemical) or in its propellant.

The range of household spraying, from "air fresheners" to bug killers (both of which pollute the air), adds to the outgassing, radon, and other stress factors imposed on our bodies. Children and ailing older persons remain at highest risk to all air contaminants.

Our neural and immune systems are stressed by crop spraying as well as spraying activities at home, business, and in the garden. The assault on our respiratory system and our detoxifying organs is vast, unpredictable, and of probable high impact to asthmatics and persons with respiratory diseases and allergic sensitivities. The Environmental Protection Agency has indicated that organophosphates such as para- thion and malathion can alter brain function and induce irritability, depression, paranoia, and difficulty in thinking, memory, and communication.

Chlorofluorocarbons (CFCs) that contribute to depletion of the earth's protective ozone layer in the stratosphere should be assiduously avoided. Scientists warn that destruction of the earth's ozone would allow increased exposure to solar ultraviolet radiation, leading to possible increased incidence of skin and other cancers and decreased agricultural productivity. The use of CFCs as a propellant for aerosol sprays was banned in the U.S. in 1978. However, their industrial production is increasing. They are used as a refrigerant (Freon) in air conditioning and other systems and in other industrial applications such as solvents and foam-blowing agents.

E.I. duPont de Nemours & Co., the firm that introduced CFCs and the world's largest producer, announced it would totally phase out all production of these chemicals. The United States Senate in 1988 ratified the Montreal Protocol, an international agreement that calls for freezing production and use of CFCs and halons at 1986 levels beginning in 1989 and to cut their use and production by 50 percent by 1999. Many researchers, environmentalists, manufacturers, and users have called for complete elimination of CFCs and halons, arguing that a 50 percent reduction does not go far enough in meeting the threat to the ozone layer. Dow Chemical Co. has announced that it is using a foaming agent in Styrofoam board and other products that does not harm the ozone layer to replace the CFCs formerly used. Other major U.S. companies have also stated they will phase out CFCs in their products and processes.

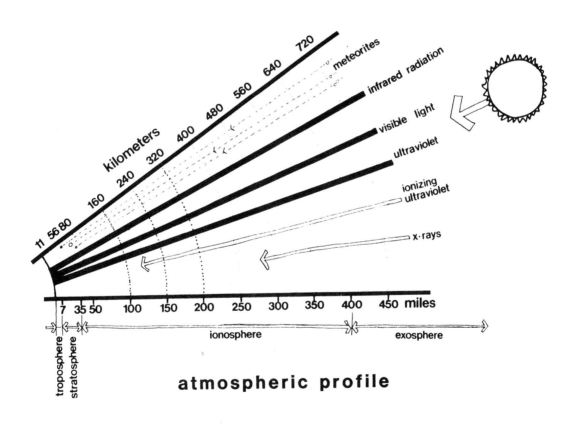

atmospheric profile

PART FIVE - CARBON EMISSIONS

PETRO-POWERED VEHICLES

Petro-powered vehicles pollute the air, spew out harmful particulates, generate noise, and are a peril to our sensitivities and state of health. The respiratory system and person within the proximity of automotive fumes are subject to their poisonous effect. The young, the very old, the ill, and the ultrasensitive are most readily distressed by the intensities of atmospheric pollution. But a risk to health is shared by all of us.

We spend more or less time within the "indoor space" of enclosed vehicles. The new car smell is a medley of toxins. Vehicles not only outgas the chemistry of their manufacture but also encapsulate the airborne emissions of other vehicles in traffic (and often exhaust of the vehicle itself) and pollutants in the localized outdoor atmosphere. Smoking in a vehicle adds a dangerous concentration to the already polluted air. Children in particular have their delicate lungs assaulted by smoking within such a confined space.

What escapes the mind of most people is that every mile driven is a demand upon extracting, transporting, refining, storing, and vending oil or its products. Every mile driven takes its toll on our local and global atmosphere and upon the threshold limits of global habitability. Mother Nature's ecology, ecosystems, and our vitality and health are lessened by the outpouring of fossil fuel gases and particulates. A growing

127

number of persons are becoming increasingly sensitive to petrochemical and other toxins in our environment.

The average driver drives about 10,000 miles per household per year (too often alone in a car). This is an exorbitant amount of travel and causes an exorbitant amount of air pollution. Not only does the consumption of fuel pollute the air but also the tires, engine oil, and wear on the highway all translate into air pollution. Roadways, parking areas, bridges, tunnels, and other facilities are accommodations to the "machine." All these elements for our automotive society represent increments of environmental denigration.

Principal relief from the toxic emissions of all classes of vehicles lies in using a "clean" burning fuel in place of gasoline or diesel. Other immediate steps to decrease our overt impact on the atmosphere are to decrease our mileage by combining destinations into one trip, driving at off-peak hours, phoning or writing instead of driving, using public transportation, walking or riding a bicycle, avoiding stop-and-go streets, and sharing a ride with someone else.

Buying high-mileage cars, avoiding car interiors with a preponderant chemical odor, and planning trips that are likely to use the least gas from destination to destination are ways to lessen the problem. As you keep your motor efficiently tuned, your exhaust system tight, and do not let your car stand and idle, your reduce air pollution. Keeping the car interior clean with nontoxic methods and frequent vacuuming reduces respiratory stress on the riders. Dog or cat dander in a vehicle can aggravate allergies and distress sensitive individuals.

Beyond automotive vehicles, petro-powered equipment for construction, industrial purposes, roadwork, as well as the ubiquitous lawn mower, sidewalk blowers, et al., should be minimally (or not at all) employed for the task at hand. In architectural planning minimal demands upon the *in situ* use of excavation and earth-moving equipment should be a fundamental consideration. Cut and fill and landforming can be most adroitly used to effectively improve the "earth energy" functions of the site with minimal air pollution. Earth should be thought of as an integral element of the architecture. The least *in situ* air pollution that is generated, the less our global atmosphere is degraded. Pushing a lawn mover is good exercise. Petro-powered outdoor mowers, blowers, and indoor forklifts and other equipment that pollute the outdoor or indoor atmosphere have a negative ecosystemic effect.

Cities are becoming so overloaded with harmful pollution that regulatory restrictions may soon be imposed on growth and initiation of new development projects. New traffic management patterns may be required that could nullify the conventional project-siting process. Federal regulations and/or severe penalties for noncompliance with air quality standards could preempt local planning and zoning authority.

Outdoor Air Pollution in a Major City

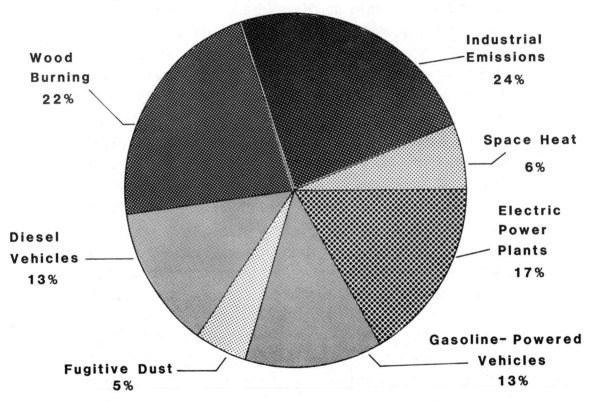

Wood Burning 22%

Industrial Emissions 24%

Space Heat 6%

Electric Power Plants 17%

Diesel Vehicles 13%

Gasoline- Powered Vehicles 13%

Fugitive Dust 5%

Denver, Colorado

AUTOMOTIVE EMISSIONS

Automotive emissions are more pervasive than generally believed. Such emissions invade houses and buildings from outdoor traffic, outdoor parking lots, and outdoor loading and unloading spaces, as well as from indoor garages and passages.

Little thought is usually given in planning and design to idling vehicles with motors running at entryways and particularly under canopies or other architectural elements that to an extent confine the fumes and result in their greater intrusion into indoor spaces. Where intake air through windows, vents, or mechanical systems might occur, the location and design of these openings should be such to avoid auto exhaust intrusion into indoor spaces. Noise from vehicles will also intrude into the interior through such openings and should be considered as a related problem.

Maintaining buildings with slight positive internal air pressure with filtered air, with air intakes as free as possible from auto emissions, should be the objective.

With judicious planning, enclosed or partially covered parking can be naturally ventilated in many cases. Natural cross ventilation, a large inflow area of outdoor air with stack action ventilation, or using inductive solar heat assist for venting can avoid costly and noisy mechanical ventilation in appropriate circumstances (if properly designed with adequate influx of acceptable replacement air). During conditions where natural ventilation is inadequate, ventilation to meet codes will be required. A CO (carbon monoxide) activated switch can be used to automatically turn on ventilation equipment in enclosed parking areas that are infrequently used or to supply mechanical ventilation for an extended time period as desired or required.

Outdoor entry porte cocheres, canopies, and building over-hangs should be designed with stack ventilation or other roof openings strategically located to lessen the concentration of fumes. Wind direction should be considered on a seasonal basis and how it might increase or decrease indoor intrusion by automotive fumes.

Garages pose a particular problem to health. Toxic fumes directly emitted from gasoline and oil evaporation and the motor vehicle have a negative effect upon the air quality of an unvented garage. Garages most often are repositories of dust, oil drippings, stored chemicals for lawn or garden, gasoline for lawn mowers or snowblowers, and sundry other sources of noxious gases and particulates offensive to our respiratory system.

Garages separated from a dwelling or building are less problematic to air quality, but when attached considerably increase the probabilities of contaminants entering into indoor spaces. Attached garages are very popular due to their convenience, personal security, freedom from the vagaries of weather, and for their economy in structure in shared construction with the architecture. They also act as a climatic shield for a portion of the house. Adequate ventilation is a number-one requirement for the removal of polluted air. For commercial and multifamily garages, regulatory codes usually set forth ventilation requirements. For the residential family garage such regulations do not prevail. In any case, air quality is compromised by the number of vehicles, their exhaust emission, and the duration of time with the motor running.

Matters of importance that should be considered "essential" when dealing with garages are:

+ cross ventilation of the garage by using a low screened vent opening with roof wind turbine that ventilates <u>away</u> from the entry door to the house

+ low and high cross-ventilating screened openings or windows can be an adequate alternative

+ a breezeway connecting the garage to a new or older residence can benefit by a weather-protecting roof and as may be elected a wood or metal grillework surround for personal safety

+ an intervening well-ventilated vestibule, storeroom, or other nonoccupied space can also serve as a "break" between a garage and indoor living space

+ the garage should be vented away from windows or other openings of the residence

+ keeping the garage interior clear of dust, oil, or other residues and toxins and using painted interior drywall or other surfaces for ceilings and sidewalls is advisable

+ leave the car windows adequately open to outgas the chemical toxins from the car interior

+ keep fire-risk and toxic-air-risk items and equipment out of the garage

+ repair work on an automobile that liberates gasoline, oil, or exhaust fumes should not be done in a closed garage

+ eliminate oil drippings from vehicles

+ keep the garage and garage floor <u>clean</u>

FIREPLACES AND STOVES

In the realm of relative air quality, conventional fireplaces and stoves appear less sinister than they actually are. Yet anything burning within the indoor atmosphere uses up valuable oxygen and contributes pollution to the air.

The outdoor atmosphere has become more polluted by the smoke from wood and other solid-fuel-burning fireplaces and stoves. Aside from burning tobacco, the smoke from such combustion can contribute to indoor pollution to a greater extent than other particulate sources within the indoor space. Wood-smoke particulates offer a similar scenario as that of radon isotope attachment to cigarette particulates.

The beauty, radiant warmth, and romantic affinity of the fireplace and visibly burning fire are trade-offs with injury to health, to energy waste, to depletion of oxygen (when outdoor air does not directly serve the combustion process), and to pollution of outdoor and indoor air. A typical wood stove operated for four hours produces the same amount of carbon monoxide as a car driven for 20 miles, according to a report by the American Lung Association of Colorado.

Conventional fireplaces pollute outdoor and indoor air, consume oxygen from room spaces, and waste energy and wood used as fuel. More heat goes up the chimney than heats the room. Energy-conserving heat exchange fireplaces and energy-efficient stoves are a better choice, particularly where they use outside air for combustion, close off the flames from the room, and use a catalytic converter or other techniques to reduce carcinogenic pollutants and smoke (can be as much as 50 to 80 percent less). In cold weather fireplace and stove flues, if not tightly closed when not in use, will rob indoor spaces of heat. Burning only thoroughly dry seasoned wood that contains little resin and building a hot fire will cause less air pollution. Oak, elm, and hemlock create less pollution than pine, fir, and eucalyptus.

Chimneys and flues by their height, size, design, and indoor location have a significant effect upon performance and buildup of creosote. Outdoor air inversions, seasonal wind patterns, roof caps, flue dampers, and the design of a fireplace or stove also affect performance. Installation should carefully follow the recommendations of the stove or fireplace manufacturer. Keep flues and chimneys clean!

Neighborhoods seriously suffer from the noxious outpourings of smoke from wood, coal, or coke-burning fires. Regulations should strictly limit the use of or, more beneficially, outlaw conventional wood-burning fireplaces and stoves. The prime necessity if use is permitted is a standard for fireplace and stove efficiency and emissions, direct outside combustion air, and regulations such as "no burn days" that prohibit use when ambient pollution levels exceed a specified concentration. Catalytic stoves or stoves with catalytic add-ons are a code requirement in some municipalities. Outside combustion air intakes for fireplaces and stoves should be tightly connected and insulated between the equipment and the outdoors. Solid fuel burning should not be treated lightly, as wood, coal, and coke also produce carcinogenic compounds and particulates. Barbecues also contribute to outdoor air pollution.

Locating high tech energy-efficient stoves and recirculative fireplaces (with outside combustion air) in a heat-retaining large thermal mass near the center of living areas favors efficiency and gives the benefit of centralized energy.

Many types and models of fireplace inserts and stoves are available. As an alternative to burning wooden logs or coal, wood pellets, dried corn (where pellets or corn are automatically fed into the firebox), or the forge principle for an intense fire (more complete combustion reducing carbon monoxide and particulates) offer cleaner burning options.

Other stove and fireplace alternative fuels are natural gas, propane, and possibly, methane. Methane is a biogas that could be generated from organic matter *in situ* or locally for heating. A home-scale system is needed. Greater imagination and creativity are needed to replace the time-honored tradition of the hearth with a nonpolluting, pleasurable substitute.

Gas logs, much touted now, have the advantage of wood-burning simulation, no ashes, a flame at a moment's notice, and little pollution. Disadvantages are cost of installation, ersatz imitation of the real thing, use of a finite petrofuel with inefficient heating, using oxygen from indoor space (except when outside combustion air is supplied), and the possible escape of gas into interior spaces. In the opinion of the author, natural gas as well as other petrofuels are too precious to burn in a fireplace.

Where permitted, particularly in areas remote from urbanization, catalytic and other relatively clean-burning stoves may be responsibly selected by the home owner. The most considerate ecologic option is to have no fireplace or stove. An exception can be when climate-responsive architecture and optimized site-specific sun, earth, air, and water energies are first employed and no other cleaner supplemental form of heating is available. As a guide to stove selection, the EPA is certifying specific brands of catalytic and other units that provide adequate secondary combustion of toxic gases. Look for an EPA certification sticker when shopping for wood stoves.

PART SIX - AIRBORNE OFFENDERS

MICROORGANISMS

Within indoor air biological organisms and pathogens can be irritating, harmful, or lethal to humans. The growth or inhibition of various microorganisms depends upon levels of relative humidity. Low relative humidities can limit growth of certain microorganisms and pathogens, but dryness of air can impair the function of cilia. The hair-like cilia, without moisture, cannot function in sweeping bacteria and other contaminants from our sinuses and bronchial tree into the digestive tract where they are eliminated.

Temperature and humidity should not only be comfortable but be controlled to assure effective immune response, as well as the suppression of aggressive microorganisms and pathogens. When indoor relative humidity is controlled in a range between 40 to 60 percent, respiratory and skin functions are optimized and asthmatic reactions are lessened (microorganisms thrive more successfully below 40 and above 60 percent relative humidity). This safer humidity zone for indoor health and a better indoor environment is also beneficial to many plants that can absorb carbon dioxide and to an extent (depending upon the type of plant) provide an output of oxygen. Plants respire water vapor that will tend to raise or sustain indoor humidity during winter when levels are lower. A negative aspect of plants is that they can contribute aero-allergens to the indoor atmosphere.

When indoor humidity is low, ozone production increases. It is an irritant of eyes and our respiratory system. It also acts catalytically to increase toxic reactions with indoor airborne chemicals. Low humidity can also make odors and airborne particles more irritating.

Positive ionization predominates in virtually all homes and buildings that is conducive to the proliferation of bacteria and viruses. Negative ionization suppresses bacterial and viral growth and thus is particularly beneficial to hospitals, nursing homes, or where sanitation is of great importance. Control measures include humidification or dehumidification required to maintain 40 to 60 percent relative humidity, elimination of substances that proliferate viruses and bacteria, adequate ventilation, temperature control, prompt removal of bacteriological waste, isolation of persons with communicable disease, cleanliness, sanitation, and negative ionization.

... a ventilating system that recirculates air in a closed environment can prolong the possibility of infection.

*-- Kevin Green in **Indoor Air Quality: An Architectural Primer,** 1984*

SWIMMING AND HOT SPA POOLS

Indoor swimming and hot spa pools are usually treated with chlorine, bromine, algicides, or other toxic chemicals. As gases, they permeate space. The rate of ventilation of the indoor space determines the airborne level of these toxic gases.

Not only are these toxic gases disagreeable in odor, but in the interests of health it is better that more desirable alternatives be used to abate air contamination.

On the reverse side of the coin, the water of swimming and particularly hot pools needs to be treated to control bacterial and algal proliferation. Not only is the water a growth medium, but usually prevalent high humidities and interior surfaces offer a conducive environment for the growth of certain bacteria, molds, and algae. Swimming pool temperatures might range from 78 to 85 degrees F, while hot tubs will be in the range of 102 to 106 degrees F. The hotter temperature of the hot pool water not only encourages some prolific bacterial and algal growth, but also contributes to higher indoor humidities that encourage such growth on warm moist surfaces.

Ventilation adequate to keep relative humidity below 60 percent and a dehumidifying system can be employed to remove moisture from the air and return it directly back to the pool. Such dehumidifying units can avoid a cold weather air tempering requirement (heating outdoor ventilation air can be energy intensive). The trade-off is the initial cost plus the operating cost versus comparative air tempering and ventilation.

Natural ventilation, when outdoor air is relatively dry and temperatures are moderate or warm, can both reduce chemical fumes, surface mold, and algal contamination and optimize energy conservation. Natural ventilation can be augmented by temperature differential inductive ventilation, venturi action, and positive and negative wind pressures.

The relationship between other indoor spaces and a pool area can have both positive and negative effects. The positive effect can be welcome humidity (when not too much with a pool cover for control) and contributory warmth when desired in cool weather for adjoining indoor spaces. The negative can be too high a contributory humidity for adjoining spaces as well as chemical, mold, or algal contamination of their air and surfaces. In most cases it is best to close off swimming and hot spa pools from indoor living areas.

Alternative methods of control over bacterial or algal proliferation in pool water include electrolysis using salt (NaCl) in the water for disassociation of chlorine and sodium atoms forming a hypochlorite, which (when properly regulated) results in no detectable odor of chlorine in the air. Other means can be by the use of ultraviolet light purification, silver ions (sometimes

144

combined with copper ions), ozone that is effective without respiratory harm, and sand or diatomaceous earth filtration used with any of the foregoing methods. Depending upon the use of a pool, chlorine may have to be periodically introduced under controlled pH conditions to supplement the foregoing means of water purification. If a pool does not have any salt in it for an electrolytic system, a filtration enhancement system is available that clusters microscopic impurities into a larger, more filterable particle size, thereby improving the efficiency of a sand or other interception-type filter.

Daily filtration of pool water is essential and can be time-clock-regulated for automatic cleaning. A turbo jet system is available that consists of underwater jets that circulate water upward from the bottom in a vortexian action. Combined with an adequately sized sand filter and water purification system, the chore of manual pool cleaning can be virtually eliminated. A properly designed pool cover kept on indoors when the pool is not in use will lessen interior surface condensation.

Indoor pools should be <u>well</u> insulated from cold outdoor temperatures and have waterproof drywall with a taped aluminum vapor barrier (on the warm interior side directly under the drywall) over thermal break rigid insulation board between the drywall and roof joists or other framing and superinsulation above. Insulation should be of the type not affected by any possibilities of moisture penetration. Tightness of the system is critical to prevent condensation within the roof and outer wall framing systems. Avoid <u>any</u>

penetrations of the system. Prestressed or conventional concrete construction can also be used and possesses the advantage of thermal mass. The indoor pool decks and the pool location and intervening sunspace or thermal glazing (clear glass or plastic) oriented to the south to receive direct solar gains (a pool cover should permit solar penetration) will provide a good energy-retaining environment.

A sunspace or greenhouse (or both) to the south can be designed to effectively temper wintertime cold air and bring in cool or warm outdoor air at other times for ventilation, reduction of humidity, and controlling the pool space temperature. Other advantages are that the sunspace or greenhouse can act as a climatic buffer and be a place for sunbathing and therapeutic warmth.

It should be noted that a hot spa pool within a sunspace benefits by direct solar radiation, but due to the 102° to 106°F temperature of the water, heavy condensation on exterior glazing can occur during winter months. Setting the glazing directly into the setting bed of an aluminum channel set directly into a tile (or other impervious material) floor will avoid the probable rotting of a wood sill.

The finish of wall and ceiling surfaces of indoor pool or spa enclosures is of ultimate importance to act as a waterproof surface, to both retard mildew and make its removal easier. A hard white epoxy surface finish has proven to be practical. Avoid all metal in the pool area that can invite rust. Nonslip dark tile over concrete for pool deck areas is practical and ideal for receiving direct solar gains.

In cool and cold climate locations the large volume of a swimming pool and smaller volume of a spa pool should be thought of as a great concentration of energy. A one-degree change in temperature represents thousands of Btus (British Thermal Units). The architecture should be designed and thermally engineered to take advantage of year-round indoor microclimates.

The author's 11,000-gallon, 100 percent solar-heated, indoor "lap" swimming pool in 10 years has not (except for a few days) been below 80°F. The original water was not drained nor the pool acid cleaned in 8-1/2 years due to an automated turbo jet system with vortex outlets in the bottom of the pool. The pool has 200 pounds of salt (pleasant to swim in) that provides sodium chloride for electrolytic chlorination. When properly regulated no chlorine odor is evident. Alkali alumina silicate/sodium and other molecular adsorbers have been tested within the pool area. Mildew that was occurring to some degree on wall surfaces around the pool has been substantially reduced by the adsorbers. Four one-quart size adsorbers were used for the swimming pool room area of approximately 700 square feet with an 8' ceiling height. The indoor pool is kept covered when the room space is not being ventilated, except for daily one-hour swimming periods.

ODORS

Indoor ventilation requirements were originally created to bring in oxygenated outdoor air and expel body odor and carbon dioxide. Odors that assault our nostrils are prescribed to be exhausted in accordance with codes and regulations. The time period of odors emanating from paints, finishes, floor coverings, wall coverings, upholstery, and household items can vary considerably within a level of relative personal tolerance.

In contrast, persistent smoking within indoor space can be a constant source of odor. Not only does the acrid odor of burning tobacco cling to interior surfaces, but it also permeates clothing, hair, and skin. Carpet and other soft fabrics of upholstery and draperies particularly retain odors from smoking for a protracted period of time. The smoke odor on fibrous surfaces of papers, documents, and fabrics can remain until they may be more thoroughly aired for a long time. Musty odors may not only be disagreeable, but can also trigger an allergic reaction in sensitive individuals.

The author "bakes out" (outgasses) magazines, furnishings, documents, clothing, and other items to remove odors and toxic fumes by means of a sunspace using direct solar radiation and profuse inductive natural ventilation. When evidence of odor is gone or barely perceptible, then such items are brought within occupied interior spaces. Care

148

should be exercised to not put items sensitive to fading, temperature, or other damage in the direct path of the sun, nor at times of excessive heat in the sunspace. As may be suitable and safe, some items could be outgassed outdoors on a porch, under an overhang, or be aired out in the open.

Most air fresheners and fragrant sprays do nothing to make indoor air more healthful: in fact, they can mask serious sources of air pollution, desensitize the olfactory senses, and also contribute to air pollution themselves by emitting harmful chemical or organic contaminants. Offensive odors are better removed by natural ventilation, with a fan, or by **source elimination**. A natural air freshener made entirely of citrus and herbal oils that has a local ionizing effect is available from some health food stores. Borax can be used to absorb and remove odors from various materials and surfaces, as well as from carpets. Packaged molecular adsorbers of zeolite (a volcanic mineral) and alkali alumina silicate/sodium can be selectively used to effectively remove odors, offensive gases, and mildew. White vinegar is useful for sanitation and odor removal from countertops, appliances, and other places where bacteria congregate. Air cleaning units with activated charcoal or an electron field generator can substantially reduce airborne odors over a period of time. The most important measure is to avoid, eliminate, or adequately attenuate odor-producing sources.

The human nose is a remarkable instrument of biologic sensitivity. It protects us from bacterial contamination and toxic gases by its discrimination. It is well to heed its olfactory warnings. Some offenders of our biologic wellness, however, emit no odor. Carbon monoxide is invisible and has no odor; the same is true for radon. Other odorless chemical gases and vapors can be irritants or toxic. Invisible airborne micro-organisms can cause disease. Radioactivity passes invisibly and without odor through the atmosphere and can penetrate and damage our body's cells.

The human body emits odors from the pores, mouth, and gastrointestinal system. We further compound the odor we carry with us by the fragrances, lotions, and other substances we apply to our body. Treated natural fiber and synthetic clothing that we wear adds to the indoor pollution. The vapors and gases can be of both natural and chemical origin. Most persons can be annoyed or repelled by the multifarious sources of odor.

Persons with asthma, allergies, or respiratory problems can seriously suffer from smoke, fragrances, molds, pollen, and chemical vapors. Indoor air should be safely breathable and reasonably pleasant for the most sensitive and reactive members of society.

PART SEVEN - INVISIBLE RADIATION

RADIOACTIVITY

Architecture is replete with standards and regulations to avert a bevy of physical hazards. But the hazards of invisible agents can quietly be more threatening than a high balcony with a broken railing.

The bombardment of human tissue by silent and invisible rays from radioactive materials fails to warn our senses that all is not well within our indoor environment. Scientists have warned, "there is no safe level of radiation."

Construction materials, principally stone, earth, brick (from radioactive clays), and concrete from radioactive constituents (particularly gravel) can have radioactive properties. Such materials can emit alpha and beta particles and gamma radiation. Alpha particles will only penetrate to subcutaneous layers of the skin. Beta particles will penetrate to depths of the order of millimeters. Gamma radiation will penetrate completely through the body. Radiation can cause injury, mutation, and death to cells of the body. The result can be a cancerous malignancy or other chronic tissue deprecations such as atherosclerosis and other pathologic lesions. Suspect materials should be tested for radioactivity before being incorporated into construction. Radioactivity of materials can be tested by laboratories using a scintillometer.

Dangerous radioactive heavy metals such as radium, thorium, and polonium, generated from coal-burning power plants, are released as fly ash to the atmosphere. These ultra-small particles can be inhaled and radioactivity remain concentrated in the bones. Coal electric-generating plants can release more harmful radiation than a nuclear power plant.

In addition to the adverse effects that occur between radon progeny and cigarette smoke, growing tobacco leaves absorb airborne radioactive elements from the soil and phosphate fertilizers. When the tobacco is burned in smoking, radioactive isotopes, especially polonium-210, are inhaled by the smoker and by anyone nearby who breathes the smoke, since at least 50 percent of the radioactive isotopes are released into the surrounding air.

Radon has been thoroughly publicized as a major indoor risk. But thoron (a 55-second half-life isotope of radium-224) can be present in structural materials and inhalation of the decay products of thoron promotes malignancy and functionally damaged cells. Thoron can have more lingering biologic effects than radon. In our food chain the persistence of radioactive isotopes taken up from the air and from the soil by plants can cause cell damage and malignant or other aberrations within our body. Radionuclides are produced naturally, but nuclear testing, processing, power generation, and other nuclear ventures add incident hazards.

Smoke alarms are required by code in many municipalities. The photoelectric type, either battery operated or wired to the house current, is advisable rather than the ionization type. The ionizing detector field is produced by radioactive americium-241 or radium-226, and it is recommended that these type of smoke alarms not be used or disposed of in the unprotected environment.

Cosmic radiation reaching Earth constantly showers us with energetic rays that for the most part harmlessly pass through our body. But a strong question arises as to the extent that heavy masses of reinforced concrete construction may attenuate the velocity of cosmic rays, resulting in biologic cellular damage. High-rise concrete and steel buildings are questionable for habitat or as a work environs. Some reports indicate that persons who dwell or work (or both) within high-rise structures can be at increased risk to fatigue, neural debilities, and other dysfunctions. But air is generally cleaner for ventilation the higher it is above traffic and other polluting sources. At high altitudes millirem exposure from the cosmic ray component can be five to ten times higher than at sea level. The annual exposure at sea level equals 26 millirems (mrem, a measurement of radiation dosage). Exposure will increase at higher elevations and as a result of jet air travel (1 mrem for every 2500 miles) because of thinner atmosphere. The annual total average radiation dose exposure in the U.S. is 180 mrems (from natural and man-made sources).

From primal times humans have been exposed to natural radiation. Our evolutionary biologic being is a result of the effect natural radiation has had upon the mitotic division of our cells as well as other environmental factors. Natural radiation from cosmic, soil, rock, and water sources and radioactive gases in the atmosphere varies with altitude, geologic features, and geopathic fields. Cosmic radiation comes from the sun and from outside the solar system. In extensive dose-equivalent millirem exposures, the radiation from manmade sources has been judged by an EPA study to significantly exceed that from natural sources.

Sources of Radiation Exposure

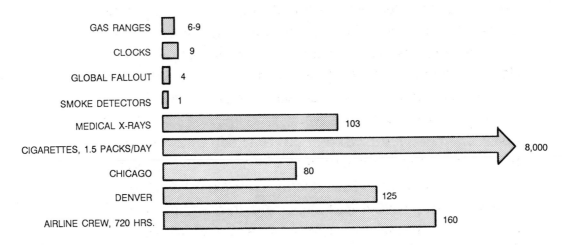

MILLIREMS PER YEAR (PER PERSON EXPOSED)

156

Greater study is needed as to the resonant, concentrating, and attenuating types and factors of radiation, as well as atmospheric effects, upon the concepts, planning, and design of architecture. The problems are multifaceted, complex, and interrelated. Relevant physiologic and psychologic realities are now poorly addressed. The dimensions of design within a holistic, ecologic, vitalizing, and life-sustaining context are critical.

ELECTROMAGNETIC ENERGIES

Electromagnetic fields cover a broad band of atmospheric, earth, cosmic, and technologically produced energies that can augment well-being or result in biologic harm. Electromagnetic energies originate from Nature and from technical processes, systems, and devices. They include <u>electric fields</u>, <u>magnetic fields</u>, and <u>electromagnetic radiation</u>. These fields exhibit spectral ranges from ultra-low to extremely high frequencies.

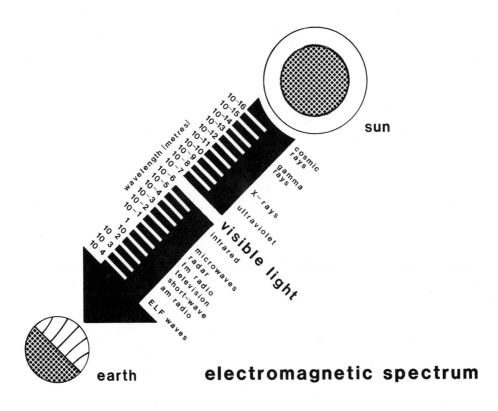

sun

earth   **electromagnetic spectrum**

158

ELF (extra low frequency) fields are not technically an air pollutant, but their biologic effect is experienced through the atmosphere. ELF fields are electromagnetic fields from 1 to 30 Hertz (cycles per second). The beneficial frequencies are in the range of 7 to 9 Hertz. Our endocrine system is agreeably stimulated by this range. ELF fields can have a profound effect upon biological systems. ELF radiation in certain frequencies is psychoactive, causing mental depression at 6.66 Hertz. Biologic disturbance and reactive behavior can occur at other exact detrimental frequencies.

Before humans made such extensive use of the spectrum ... there was a narrow band in the extra low-frequency (ELF) region, ranging from 1 to 30 Hertz, which was produced by resonance among the earth's surface, the magnetic field, and the ionosphere. The only other electromagnetic radiation of any magnitude was in the 1,000 Hertz range, produced by lightning discharges; the remainder of the spectrum was empty. All life began and has evolved in this relatively constant electromagnetic environment over the past three billion years.

Theoretical analysis of the electromagnetic field that existed ... when life began indicates that enormous amounts of energy were present in the ELF region, particularly around the 10-Hertz frequency. It is interesting, in this regard, that the brain-wave pattern of all animals, from earth worms to humans, lies in this ELF range.

-- Robert O. Becker, "Brain Pollution," in Psychology Today, Feb. 1979

It was revealed in 1976 that ELF magnetic fields, in seven years of laboratory testing for the U.S. Navy, can alter the function of the cells and cell chemistry; can inhibit or enhance bone growth, cell dedifferentiation, RNA synthesis and processes, and DNA transcription processes; can entrain human brain waves; and can cause disorientation. ELF magnetic fields are not appreciably attenuated by distance.

ELF radiation has an insidious military significance. It has been implemented by the U.S. Navy at a Great Lakes location to effectively communicate with naval submarines. The Air Force has projected the concept of a nationwide low frequency "Ground Wave Emergency Network" of about 200 towers designed to survive a nuclear strike and transmit messages between top U.S. political and military leaders and Air Force strategic bases in the event of nuclear war. The Russians, for an extended period, have been researching ELF effects upon disorientation of the human nervous system. Noted effects can be nausea, uncontrollable emotional weakness, and dizziness.

On the brighter side, Nature's pulsating fields in the 7 to 9 Hertz range are salutary to human vitality. These outdoor fields of magnetic and pulsating positive electric resonance (Schumann resonance) are intercepted by the structural members of a building. When replicated indoors with equipment that generates these fields, they can enhance biologic vitality. Combined with negative ionization (that also occurs naturally outdoors), these fields raise the level of awareness and provide a notable freshness to the indoor air.

60-cycle electrical power of homes and buildings projects electric and magnetic fields that are counter to the biologic frequencies of our brain and bodies. Wiring in grounded metallic conduit is advisable in sleeping quarters and places where persons might spend a prolonged time. We benefit biologically when the electric field is grounded with a conduit, but the magnetic field that <u>penetrates</u> the conduit can do greater harm to the cell membranes of our body. An ordinary electric clock emits undesirable electric and magnetic fields. Electric blankets, heating pads, heater elements of water beds, and other "close" or "contact" devices that induce electric and attendant magnetic fields are sources of probable biologic risk. Electrical gear and equipment that produce appreciable magnetic fields should be located away from occupant areas. Studies have shown there is 300 to 3,000 times more alternating current radiation in an average home with electricity and appliances than outdoors in a rural area at a distance from power lines.

Electromagnetic waves from microwave ovens can be biologically harmful, and they should always be tested for possible radiation leakage. Television sets can emanate X-rays and CRT (cathode ray tube) scanning systems, which can generate up to 40,000 volts, have a propensity to emit low-level radiation. Close human proximity is questionable.

Widespread usage of CRT-type video display terminals (VDTs) has led to VDT Operator's Distress Syndrome. Many of these machines exhibit an excessive positive charge on the outer surface of the display, resulting in severe depletions of negative ions in proximity of the screen. This ion deprivation effect has produced a number of adverse biologic symptoms and physiological stress. Reported symptoms include headache, hypersensitivity, irritability, depression, heightened perception of neck and back pain, fatigue, reduced productivity, shortened attention span, sleep disturbances, and pregnancy difficulties. Another aspect reported by Dr. Gerald Rappe, member of the International Institute of Environmental Sciences, is that the highly positive electric field of a VDT induces a polarity change in the skin of a person working within 10 or 12 inches of the screen. Bacteria and viruses that are net electro-negative are attracted by the dominant positive field from the VDT and are drawn to the skin of the worker's face and hands. One recommended remedy is a glare filter fabricated from a conductive-coated nylon mesh, grounded so as to keep the CRT display at zero potential, along with a bipolar ion generating system with a positive to negative ion ratio of 1:2.

More concern should be given to prevalent computer and other high tech devices used by children, as well as by adults and pregnant women. Computer electromagnetic fields are not benign. While definitive proof of biologic harm needs more study, it stands to reason that when we violate the electrodynamics of the body, we do so at a level of risk. The fields from computers and appliances rapidly decrease in intensity by distance as compared to power line fields that extend to a greater extent in space.

High power transmission lines, equipment, and transformers generate a less than providential magnetic field. The best insurance is not to build homes or buildings within the proximity of such magnetic fields. In such locations outdoor activities present a potential biologic risk. While power line electrical fields can be attenuated as much as 90% by the structure of a home, the associated magnetic fields largely retain their intensity. The intensity of electromagnetic radiation varies inversely as the square of the distance. Thus as we increase our distance from a magnetic source, we decrease our degree of probable biologic harm. It is advisable to bury power lines to homes and buildings.

Our brain and body form an electromagnetic and ionizing biologic organism. Our brain and organic cells all have a cyclic vibration. As reported in <u>Biological Effects of Power Frequency Electric and Magnetic Fields</u> (see references), the cells of our body have definitive electric fields across their cellular membranes. Such naturally occurring fields tend to be 100 times or more intense than those usually encountered from power-frequency fields. But low-energy power-frequency fields of relatively weak magnitude at bio-critical definitive levels can cause perturbations at the cellular level that can interfere with the bio-integrity and functioning of animal cells.

We live literally in a sea of electromagnetic energy that we do not sense. High frequency fields occur from extensive techno-science civilian and military sources. Evidence suggests these massive electromagnetic fields may be a pervasive health hazard, "producing stress, disease, and other harmful effects all over the world by interfering with the most basic levels of brain functioning." (Becker, op. cit.) Becker notes that radiation-induced stress could produce an increase in conditions such as hypertension and behavioral abnormalities; in cancer and other degenerative diseases related to decreased efficiency of the immune system; and new maladies from previously nonpathogenic organisms such as (possibly) Legionnaire's Disease and Reye's Syndrome.

How the total living organism of our body may be affected by the variant intensities, field frequencies, duration, and total biostress from a single or multiple number of electromagnetic sources remains speculative. But dose-related electromagnetic exposures plus other airborne and environmental stressors compound the probability of biologic harm.

Studies are being made on the "whole body" effect of electromagnetic fields as well as at the cellular level. Concerns being addressed include biologic, metabolic, learning, behavioral, circadian rhythm, and hormonal categories of effects using epidemiological evidence and other evaluative techniques.

Field elimination, avoidance, or effective attenuation remain critical to reducing ecologic and biologic levels of risk. Within the above-cited document, the Office of Technology Assessment of the United States Congress suggests the following steps could be taken to reduce human exposure to 60 Hertz fields:

> + attempt to route new transmission lines as to avoid people;

> + widen transmission line rights-of-way;

> + develop designs for distribution systems that minimize the associated electromagnetic fields;

> + develop new approaches to house wiring to minimize electrical and magnetic fields; and

> + redesign appliances to minimize or eliminate fields.

... the impact of living in electronically wired environments spreads to everything from the brain function to chromosomal characteristics of our offspring.

*-- Hal Levin, University of California at Berkeley in **AIA Journal**, Oct. 1979*

It is unlikely that the energy fields of Nature, except geopathic anomalies emanating at specific junctures from the earth, have a significant contrary impact upon our general state of health.

In comment, we are all <u>earth</u> creatures. When we isolate and separate ourselves from or build structures counter to terrestrial and atmospheric vibratory resonant frequencies, we lessen our body's magnetic resonance and vitality.

[For a reference summary of the principles of electromagnetic energies, see pages 230-237].

GEOBIOLOGIC ENERGIES

From ancient times geobiologic energies of the earth have been experienced and located as to their contrary or beneficial field effect upon people. Contrary and malady-producing geopathic emanations are caused by the disturbed fields of underground water courses and geologic fissures and formations. The electromagnetic radiation emanates into the atmosphere where fields intersect, and an aberrant or salutary biologic response can result.

Research of the Baubiologie Institute of Germany has revealed a high incidence of cancer and other biophysical dysfunctions where persons spent daily hours of time (such as in a relatively fixed position in bed or at a workplace) in the vortexian intersection of such disturbed fields. Curative results have been obtained by the moving the bed or other place of protracted position out of points of risk.

It is curious that cats will seek out these highly charged points of geopathic energy while dogs shun them and will lie or sleep out of their vortexian field. Some geobiologic research is progressing in the United States and Canada. It appears that with some techniques, the aberrant fields can be moved, thereby relieving causes of affliction and avoiding moving a bed or place of work. The author is engaged in the study and investigation of these fields identified as the negative (anomalies), the positive (beneficial), the Hartmann grid, and

167

Curry grid. A profile of the earth fields can be picked up by a geomagnetometer and be drawn by a computer graphic plotter. The greater the peaks and valleys recorded by the geomagnetometer, the greater is the probability that at such points there exists a corresponding biologic disturbance and possible harm. Dowsers using L-shaped bent rods can locate the "good" and "bad" vortexian intersections of these fields. Dowsing originated from awareness of and bio-response to weak electromagnetic field patterns.

Keep in mind that dowsing for water, magnetic fields, and other subsurface conditions is an ancient art. Dowsing can be more revealing than detection instruments. But instruments and their readouts are more convincing. After negative geopathic fields and their intersections are determined by instrumentation, a dowser, or both, the fields may be intercepted or otherwise be moved to where they no longer prevail *in situ* as a risk. Some dowsers have demonstrated intervention or field relocation with considerable success. There is mounting evidence that individuals suffering from geopathic symptoms and maladies have had relief and a curative experience when the fields are relocated or persons move away from the interception points.

It should be noted that civilizations of the past such as the Celts and the Druids located dolmens and other sacred structures in relation to these energies. In Europe and Asia religious sanctuaries, cathedrals, and other buildings were constructed in regard to the emanation of earth fields and their vortexian energy intersections. Chartres Cathedral in France is a good example. Contemporary testing of the fields within this sacred structure reveal their presence, high intensity, and locational accord. Feng Sui is still practiced in China today. It is the art of expediently using the earth's energy for the good fortune and well-being of the building occupants.

Our health, vitality, and well-being are undoubtedly influenced by our contact with the earth, its geobiologic fields, and the atmosphere as charged with the emanations from the earth and the cosmos. The electromagnetic propensities of our body at 7.83 Hertz and the vortexian DNA molecule that programs our being and organic definition correspond to the cosmos and the earth. All life on earth originated and prospers within the Schumann resonant field. It has been demonstrated that vitality and healing are stimulated and invigorated by the variant spectrums of solar, earth, water, and atmospheric energies.

It is likely that our ancient ancestors were in harmony by instinct with salutary and contrary geobiologic fields. Birds and other creatures of the sea and earth reveal their correspondence with the earth's magnetic field. In any case, many persons today can in one way or another be consciously sensitive to these fields.

In general it appears that women prefer (or at least seem to be better off in) low-intensity fields, while men can more readily not be overstressed by somewhat greater peaks.

While geobiologic fields do not appear to be attenuated by building height, the type of construction with steel or reinforced concrete can have a biologic effect.

We all have a personal connection with the forces of the Earth. Our vitality depends upon our physical and spiritual harmonic response to geobiologic, solar, and atmospheric energies. Architecture largely isolates us from these primal energies that through millennia conditioned our evolutionary form and biologic attributes. Today we principally exist within an artificial environment that departs from our essential link with the primal energies of sun, earth, air, and water. Our biologic being is ever recharged by global atmospheric and geobiologic energies.

Dr. A. Michrowski, president of The Planetary Association for Clean Energy, Inc. of Canada, gives the cogent warning that life-supportive Schumann electromagnetic resonance is being dampened by continuing electrochemical disturbances caused by man-made frequencies. The ecologic viability of human, animal, and plant life is critically threatened by technologic electromagnetic stresses. Genetic reproduction, conditions of health, ecologic and societal well-being, and upper atmospheric sustainability can be at serious risk.

PART EIGHT - REMEDIES

VENTILATION

Ventilation is an age-old means of bringing fresh oxygenated outdoor air into the interior of a home or building. It traditionally provides breathable air for the occupants, the removal of stale air, and combustion air for cooking and heating. Ventilation is a general remedy to reduce indoor air pollution. The best procedure, however, is **removal of the source of the pollution**. Ventilation is directly dependent upon the level of air purity of the outdoor air. Local pollution sources, such as fumes from toxic waste leakage, fireplaces, a neighboring industrial plant, a heavily trafficked highway, or crop spraying can render outdoor air unacceptable for indoor ventilation. Unacceptable outdoor air remains unacceptable for indoor air ventilation. In urban or other locations where variant outdoor air pollution occurs, it is advisable to constantly monitor prevailing levels. Ventilation for indoor needs should be regulated to correspond to times when outdoor air quality is best. Otherwise, effective air filtration systems should be in operation when indoor air predominantly is recirculated.

Effective filtration of indoor space has a direct relationship to indoor air volume, persistence of indoor air contaminants and radioactivity, outdoor air quality, natural or mechanical rates of ventilation, occupational activity, position of ventilation openings, and interior spatial design.

Bio-Response

Ventilation should be optimized for isolated smoking, commercial toxic or odoriferous processes, spaces subject to bacterial and viral contamination, and in other indoor spaces that present a respiratory hazard. Within the home, business, or institution, the generation of harmful gaseous, particulate, and radioactive substances requires appropriate rates of ventilation for their removal. Emissions from workshops, artwork, craftwork, copy machines, cooking, cleaning products, et al., can by their increment of added indoor pollution affect very sensitive persons and have a less noticeable negative effect upon others.

When outdoor air becomes badly polluted it is a matter of critical judgment as to the relative respiratory impact measured against the prevailing indoor sources of pollution and the need for oxygenation. The choice is a difficult one for respiratory-sensitive and dysfunctional individuals. Local attrition upon breathing can be provoked by the acrid fumes of fireplaces and barbecues.

A procedure for homes that can make urban and suburban living more tolerable is to ventilate well when outdoor air is good and "acceptable," then to button up the house and use ionization and "layered" filtration (filter media in layers for appropriate sequential filtration) to internally clean and revitalize the indoor air.

... an inadequate ventilation rate is by far the most likely cause of deteriorating indoor air quality.

> *-- Jan Stolwijk, Yale University, in Proceedings of the 3rd International Conference on Indoor Air Quality and Climate, 1984*

No single ventilation rate can assure acceptable indoor air quality in all buildings under all situations because the source strength of air contaminants varies tremendously from one building to another.

> *-- Energy Design Update, Feb. 1984*

Persons with respiratory and allergy problems often feel better in an air-conditioned environment. Mechanical refrigerated HVAC systems cool by removing moisture from the air and by lowering its temperature. Under less humid conditions and excluding (for the most part) outdoor pollens, with an indoor reduction of molds and spores, respiratory conditions and allergies are less aggravated. It is likely that the mind also perceives the cool air as "refreshing" and therefore more conducive to well-being.

Tight Construction

Older homes and buildings often have such large infiltration rates that the expeditious dilution of indoor air pollution considerably reduces respiratory risk. However, infiltration escalates energy demand.

Today's "tight" energy-efficient homes and buildings have a relatively low energy demand and tend to have a minimal ventilation rate. Minimal ventilation can lead to the "sick building syndrome" or buildings with a propensity toward occupant illness. Most mechanical systems do not effectively ventilate, by failing to adequately filter out outdoor air pollutants or to remove or filter accumulating indoor air pollutants. Lack of negative ionization and oxygenation of air and inadequate removal of carbon dioxide can exacerbate comfort and health problems.

Fume Producers

Ventilation is most effective in exhausting tobacco smoke and smoke from cooking and various processes when it is confined to a space essentially closed off from other spaces in which such activities do not occur. Make-up (replacement) air can be taken from outdoor air directly or indirectly through other noncontaminated spaces that allow intake of outdoor air (preferably under controlled and human comfort conditions). Smoking and other fume-producing activities should be confined to rooms expressly designed and prepared for the isolated ventilation these activities demand. Single occupant private offices and room spaces can be so prepared.

Molds

Adequate ventilation and sunshine can reduce indoor moisture levels (sunspaces can help to remove moisture from the air). Mold is very prolific. Dryness is essential. Dehumidification can be assisted by mechanical dehumidifiers or portable heaters. To suppress mold, some natural and synthetic chemical products (such as Borax or others chemically antagonistic to mold) are less likely to distress a sensitive individual or contribute to allergies or respiratory or environmental difficulties. Humid climates and seaside locations can pose a particular problem. Thorough ventilation of high-moisture-source indoor spaces (such as bathrooms, utility rooms, kitchens, swimming pools, hot spas) is advisable. Showers and bathtubs are especially prone to the growth of molds. A shower design by the author avoids the usual mold around shower doors or curtains. Constant attention to observe and promptly remove mold can avert a greater aggravation.

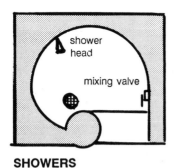

SHOWERS

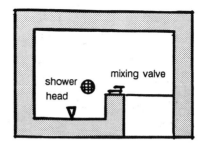

Glazed tile showers designed to avoid use of mildew-encouraging shower curtain or door.

177

Mold that grows in decaying vegetation or under other outdoor conditions gives off spores that can invade indoor spaces with incoming ventilation air. Cleaning up outdoors can be as important as cleaning up indoor sources of mold.

Cross Ventilation

Natural cross ventilation, either horizontally through indoor space or more effectively from low intake (of relatively unpolluted outdoor air) to high outlet of the flow-through air, will reduce indoor pollution. Natural ventilation requires close architectural attention. Incoming outdoor air should pass diagonally through a room space or through adjoining room spaces for effective cross ventilation. Door, window, vent, and interior openings (such as light wells and stairways) should adhere to the diagonal cross ventilation concept. When air can be introduced very low and be exhausted very high out of interior spaces the rate of airflow is improved.

Inasmuch as windows and patio doors may be placed for outdoor views, privacy, daylighting, indoor planning arrangements, and solar and climatic response, cross-ventilation outdoor air vents can be more strategically sized and located to avoid conflicts with drapes, vertical blinds, or other window treatments. Screened, louvered, or other security doors for entry, rooms, or bedrooms with solid inner doors for air control can serve well for cross ventilation.

Inductive roof stacks, venturi stacks, solar chimneys, wind turbines, and design of the architecture can act for efficient natural cross ventilation. Architectural plan configurations, spatial volumes, size, position, and control over interior openings and interior furnishings have an influence on cross ventilation as well as inductive airflows. Prevailing seasonal winds should not be neglected as an important consideration in ventilation and cross ventilation.

Inductive Ventilation

Inductive ventilation is produced by controlled interior air flows that result from temperature differentials. Positive and negative interior atmospheric pressures induced by wind movement have an influence upon ventilation through windows, doorways, and vents.

As direct sunlight pours in through glazed openings, interior convective air currents are set in motion. Heated air rises, and cooler air within the space flowing closer to the floor displaces the warmer air. In such manner homes and buildings can become literal internalized natural heat pumps.

Although internal measures can decrease the effect of indoor polluted air, displacement of interior air by outdoor air remains a principal means of ventilation and air oxygenation.

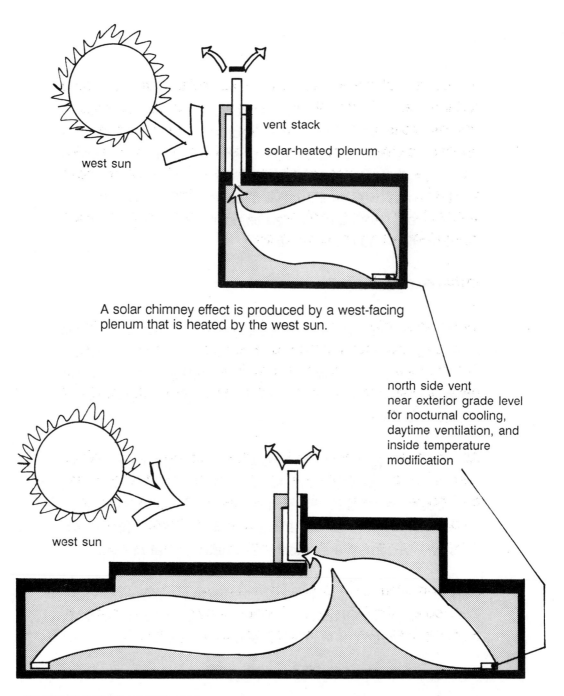

west sun

vent stack

solar-heated plenum

A solar chimney effect is produced by a west-facing
plenum that is heated by the west sun.

north side vent
near exterior grade level
for nocturnal cooling,
daytime ventilation, and
inside temperature
modification

west sun

PASSIVE SOLAR VENTILATION when outdoor temperatures are cool or moderate.

180

Air Tempering

Outdoor air is often too cold or too hot to be introduced into indoor space without tempering it for indoor comfort. This air can be preheated by a sunspace, solar thermal mass retention, by internal waste heat, warmth of the earth, or by mechanical heat or a heat exchanger. This air can be cooled by earth temperatures, through a cool basement (when radon isn't present), by evaporation, fountains and mist sprays of water, or by mechanical means.

"Bake-Out"

In new buildings or renovations, a "bake-out" of the building prior to occupancy can be effective to release and remove toxic gases of the architectural interior and its furniture, equipment, and furnishings (this is a requirement in Sweden for new public buildings). Materials used in construction and finishing will outgas organic pollutants that will drop by a factor of 10 in about one month. It takes about one year to appreciably lower moisture levels from new building construction and other chemical contaminants, including formaldehyde. Ventilation should be maximized during this period. Tests in California of the 100°F "bake-out" of a new county building found that unwanted gases declined 40 percent in 3-1/2 days. A month later they were at six percent of the original level.

The concept has merit to protect the occupants of homes and buildings, but in the process judgment is required not to injure any of the interior cabinetry, et al., with excess or prolonged heat. Completion of homes and buildings should be planned for spring and summer times of maximum natural ventilation so as not to impact mechanical systems and to benefit from such economy. Mechanical duct systems, filters, and filter housings can become contaminated by using them for a "bake-out." Release and effective removal of indoor toxins and particulates to the outdoors by ventilation should be the prime objective. The "bake-out" can considerably expedite the process. After occupancy, ventilation rates should be maximized compatible with comfort and energy cost for a period of one year or longer as may be desirable.

A recent study at the Georgia Tech Research Institute in Atlanta found that a three-day bake-out at 90°F of modular room partitions and particle board samples failed to eliminate the smell and offgassing of volatile organic chemicals emanating from the materials. The tests found that offgassing rates at the end of the bake-out were hardly lower than pre-bake emissions, even though significant quantities of the volatiles were driven off by the process. The researcher, Charlene W. Bayer, suggests that rather than letting new products outgas in people's living and work spaces, manufacturers should allow them to volatilize for several months in their warehouses before the products are sold.

Venturi and Wind Turbine Ventilation

Inductive venturi ventilation functions by an airstream flowing across a restricted aperture that induces a flow of air within a pipe or duct by edge-effect negative pressure. Some standard nonpowered venturi ventilators are available, designed for flue and duct applications. They depend upon wind as the driving force to induce ventilation of the flue or duct.

Wind turbines are also activated by wind to exhaust attic or room spaces or provide "whole" interior ventilation. These devices can be used to remove attic heat and to vent bathrooms, shower spaces, and utility rooms as well as room spaces or larger interior areas (as building codes may allow).

To serve larger indoor spaces with relatively large air volumes, the author has designed custom venturi ventilators to accord with (often complex) factors of induced ventilation. Regardless whether using venturi, wind turbine, or ordinary stack action ventilation, a manual or motorized means is essential for convenient closure of the inductive exhaust system. Effective design of inductive ventilation systems calls for professional assistance of a mechanical engineer or architect.

Mechanical Ventilation

Mechanical ventilation offers more positive means to expel and lessen the buildup of indoor air pollution. Every exhaust fan in operation will remove some of the undesired contaminants and particulates. It is of particular importance that cigarette smoke and other forms of indoor pollution be considered as to the rate of exhaust, location of exhaust, and position and vent size for incoming air adequate for the space where the pollution originates (it is advisable that polluted air not be drawn through non- or lower-polluted areas).

Ventilation rates are generally expressed in air changes per hour (ACH) or in cubic feet of air per person. The consideration of air changes for light to heavy cigarette smoking expressed in 1 to 5 minutes is relative to 12 to 60 ACH. Other nonpolluted areas and spaces of a home or building could have in energy-conserving architecture only .5 or less ACH. Cubic feet of air per person under nonpolluted conditions might be as low as 3 cubic feet of air per minute (cfm), but be as high as 7 cfm or more depending upon the level of air contamination and activity level of the occupants. ASHRAE has increased air-circulation standards from the present 5 cfm to 15 cfm for various indoor activities.

Building codes and regulations dictate indoor ventilation requirements, but have usually not addressed the full and crucial matter of indoor air quality.

Central Heating, Ventilation, and Cooling Systems

Most commercial and institutional buildings depend upon central mechanical heating, ventilating, and air conditioning

(HVAC) systems. Various types of central HVAC systems are zoned to balance the thermal conditions of the building. Most homes have central heating systems that primarily recirculate the indoor air by means of ductwork to interior spaces. Whereas almost all commercial and institutional buildings have refrigerated air conditioning, a lesser number of homes have this capability. Some older homes use piped hot water systems and steam for wintertime space heating.

From an indoor air quality standpoint, ducted systems with central forced-air heating and air conditioning have positive and negative attributes. Since commercial buildings are required by code to have ventilation, it becomes a function of a central system. In most modern buildings without operable windows, indoor air is mostly recirculated, with engineered increments of outdoor air used for ventilation. Positive aspects of a central system are its simplicity and practical and cost-effective delivery of heated, cooled, and in buildings, ventilation air. One or more HVAC units and duct distribution systems may be employed. But for homes and buildings, the filters (except in "clean rooms" and for special purposes) are inevitably inadequate to clean the air and have no capability for appropriate ionization. Additionally, HVAC systems were never designed to remove organic contaminants such as benzene, formaldehyde, etc. According to EPA research, the typical HVAC system can at best remove only 10 percent of airborne contaminants.

Electrostatic filters will not provide desirable negative ionization and tend to produce undesirable ozone. But with charcoal filtration downstream from the electrostatic unit, ozone will be adsorbed and the combination of filters will greatly improve air quality over conventional methods. Ductwork can harbor pathogenic microorganisms and mold and also ground off any desirable negative ionization produced within indoor spaces. Ductwork is also cumbersome and space-consuming within the construction. Where supply and return outlets are placed is critical to comfort and health. Being near the more polluted return air is much less desirable than being on the supply side. But in any case, all indoor pollutants are diluted to some extent as outdoor ventilation is provided, but the system will distribute the contaminants back into indoor spaces.

In addition to disagreeable patterns of forced air movement with mechanical systems, noise can be a disturbing factor (particularly in the quietness of a home). A tendency to overcool indoor spaces during hot weather with air conditioning can put a contrary stress upon persons with cardiovascular or other physical problems who go from indoors to the hot outdoors.

The greatest drawback to all mechanical HVAC systems is their utility energy demand that translates into air pollution at the power plant. Freon used for air conditioning is a chlorofluorocarbon that has been indicted as a major cause of atmospheric ozone depletion.

Using an "economizer cycle" for an HVAC system saves money in electric utility demand and provides maximum outdoor ventilation when outdoor temperatures are at an acceptable level. The bottom line is that mechanical systems powered by photovoltaic cells that would principally use *in situ* energies of the sun, air, earth, and water as well as all internal thermal loads would be an environmental advantage. The intereffect seriousness of smoking, contaminant-producing office equipment, and industrial and other air-polluting processes and sources upon an HVAC system demand special attention in all details of system design. Room-type and portable air-cleaning machines are affected in performance by mechanical HVAC systems. The effect by central systems within occupant spaces of distributing indoor pollutants and stirring them up has a concordant impact upon resultant air purification and air vitality.

Heat Exchangers

Air-to-air heat exchangers can provide a positive air supply for indoor space while reducing energy loss by the temperature exchange between exhausted indoor air and incoming outdoor air. They are particularly applicable for adequate ventilation air of "tight" construction homes and buildings.

Their advantage lies in ventilation to reduce the level of indoor air contaminants (generally exceeding those present in outdoor air), exhaust of radon and other harmful gases, control over indoor air pressure (a slight positive pressure lessens radon emissions from the earth but a tight vapor barrier of the exterior walls is essential to prevent damaging condensation within them), and oxygenated air for breathing or other needs. The disadvantages can be condensation within the unit, power requirements to operate it, maintenance, and disadvantageously locating it as to indoor space use.

Attic Fans

Attic (whole-house ventilation) fans can provide centralized or partial area indoor air exhaust ventilation. They can be used for daytime or nocturnal cooling when daytime or nighttime temperatures are in an acceptable range. Outdoor intake air can be adjusted as desired by vents, windows, or other openings. These fans, however, tend to be noisy, require considerable horsepower, and also increase the indoor emanation of radon from the soil by negative pressure. They can in hot weather effectively remove stratified hot air near the ceiling and exhaust indoor air contaminants. On the other side of the coin, they can also draw in outdoor airborne dust, pollen, and smoke from barbecues. Exhaust fans can also be installed to strictly ventilate attics.

Vortex Fans

Portable vortex fans can aid ventilation, nocturnal and daytime cooling, and wintertime destratification of warm air near the ceiling for energy efficiency and thermal comfort. They function on a natural vortex principle, hence their high level of efficiency in air movement with relatively low energy demand. They project with considerable directional force (adjustable as to angle direction) a spiral column of air. Placed at vent or window openings, they can bring in outdoor ventilation air.

Ceiling Fans

Ceiling fans, often known as Casablanca fans, can contribute to indoor comfort and in conjunction with negative ionization can reduce radon when it is present. In winter warm air stratified near the ceiling can be distributed downward to conserve energy and improve comfort. The demand on cooling systems can be lessened by a reverse-flow ceiling fan that cools by increasing evaporation from the skin.

For safety, ceiling fans should be mounted with not less than a 7-foot clearance under the rotating blades and be no more than 9 feet above floor level. Any activity in the space should be clear of the fan in operation. The fan should be safely installed to a structural member.

The blades should not be less than 6 inches wide at the tips and should pitch at least 10 degrees. A multispeed reversing type ceiling fan is most desirable for best performance under prevailing indoor conditions. Most ceilings are 8-feet high, and the blades should be at least a foot from the ceiling for greatest effectiveness. Extensions and adapter kits are available for higher and sloping ceilings. A high-quality fan with a self-lubricating motor is recommended.

189

When selecting a fan, the proportions, size, and ceiling height of a room must be considered. Recommendations are a 36- to 42-inch fan for rooms that are nearly square and not over 12 feet by 12 feet. For larger rooms and spaces up to 12 feet by 18 feet, 48- to 52-inch fans are appropriate. 60-inch fans can work well in larger areas and rooms with greater than an 8-foot ceiling height. Location at or near the center of the room is generally most effective. But when a room has a long rectangular proportion (over 18 feet), two medium-sized fans are a better choice. Fans should be placed so that blades are at least 24 inches from a wall, tall furniture, or other objects to prevent wobbling or other unwanted vibration. (Note: most of the above material was adapted from an article by John Warde, a writer for The New York Times.)

Nocturnal Cooling and Ventilation

In climates with hot daytime temperatures and cool nights, pressurized mechanically powered filtered air cooling has distinct advantages. Nighttime cooling in spaces that are not occupied during such hours and buttoning up a house during the day when hot temperatures prevail is a most effective way to achieve indoor comfort at low cost. Nocturnal cooling with a filter most appropriate to specific conditions of harmful outdoor air particulates is advisable over attic fans (that usually require greater horsepower) in delivering cleaner outdoor air to indoor spaces. Static electric filters (see the next section on air cleaning) that do not require electricity are appropriate for such mechanically pressurized air-intake ventilation and cooling systems. HEPA filters require considerably more energy to operate.

Factors that influence the effectiveness of pressurized ventilation include: interior air volume, general floor plan, partitions that divide space, furniture arrangements, window or vent locations (that can act as exhaust ports), and where the filtered outdoor air is introduced into the interior.

A variable-speed, quiet squirrel cage blower from 1500 to 3000 cfm for about 2000 square feet of indoor space is suitable for nocturnal or daytime cooling. Intake of outdoor air should be designed to avoid outdoor pollution sources. Mechanically pressurized cooling and ventilation can also be selectively used, sized, and filtered for specific small or large indoor spaces.

AIR CLEANING

Relative to the kind and number of pollutants prevailing in indoor air, most filters and filtration systems are inadequate. The combination of slightly to grossly polluted outdoor air needed to ventilate indoor space, plus the irritants and toxins from indoor smoking and outgassing of other materials, along with a dismaying range of dust and other particles and a conducive environment for potentially harmful microorganisms demand in-depth strategies to secure even a minimal level of satisfactory indoor air quality.

Kinds of filters and types of filter systems need to be addressed. The basic types of filters are: common fiber type used mainly to intercept large particles, HEPA filters usually of a convoluted design to prevent very small particles from passing through, activated charcoal filters to adsorb odors and some contaminants, electrostatic (electrically activated) filters to charge particulates with a positive charge so they are grounded as the air passes by a negatively charged plate, a new type of catalytic filter that will function at room temperatures, and potassium permanganate filters that will selectively filter out various gaseous chemicals. Air ionization units also exist that remove particles by imparting a negative charge to them so they are grounded off to room surfaces or positively charged plates. A new electron generator uses a negative field "cascade" effect that neutralizes the preponderant number of positive ions on surfaces and in the air, which coalesce and by increased weight fall to the floor by gravity and magnetic attraction.

Most filters operate on a multi-pass basis, i.e. the indoor air must pass through the filter more than once to be effectively cleaned. Effective single-pass filters are needed, particularly when bringing outdoor air into indoor spaces. A self-energized static electric single-pass filter is available that can function with natural ventilation (described later in this section). Microorganic filters are also needed in which bacteria or other microorganisms might be used to purify or oxygenate the air. A conversion from CO (carbon monoxide) to CO_2 (carbon dioxide) is possible with soils bacteria. The conversion of CO_2 to O_2 (oxygen) can be accomplished with indoor plants. Consider, however, that plants can generate spores, molds, and pollens that can aggravate allergies. These can, however, be intercepted by a static electric filter (that is not electrically activated) in venting greenhouse air into living or work space areas.

Electrostatic Filters

In electrostatic filtration air passes across positively charged wires, and the positively charged particulates are attracted to and deposit on negatively charged plates. They require an electrical connection and frequent cleaning to reduce sparking and to remove particles by washing the filters. Although electrostatic filters effectively remove very small (down to .01 micron) particles, they also produce ozone by the sparking

193

action of particles on the charged mesh. Ozone can be injurious to the human respiratory system. To alleviate this problem and to arrest gaseous elements in the airstream, an activated charcoal filter should be located in the path of the air discharged through the electrostatic filter. These filters are available in various sizes for both central forced-air heating, cooling, and ventilating systems and for portable air cleaning units.

Static Electric Single-Pass and Multi-Pass Filters

Static electric filters clean the air by air-velocity-induced static electricity through fine mesh plastic screens. They can be employed as effective filters in central forced-air HVAC systems. They can be installed to filter outdoor intake air using a blower or a fan for indoor daytime or nocturnal pressurized ventilation. A 70-percent efficient static electric filter is available that can be used to filter outdoor air by means of natural ventilation without blower or fan power. No electrical connection is necessary. The filters should be cleaned with a water jet spray every 60 to 90 days or oftener, depending upon use and filtration conditions.

While intercepting airborne contaminants reasonably well, such filters will have little effect on very small submicron particles and no effect on noxious outdoor air gases. When intake air openings are coupled with powered fans or blowers, the static electric filters can have greater density and hence be more effective in contaminant interception. Partial or full closure of intake air openings has to be considered and planned for. Wintertime cold air intrusion must be avoided. Single-pass filters can be effectively used for sunspace and greenhouse air tempering of indoor living and working spaces. They can be located to directly filter incoming outdoor air and also act to filter molds and plant spores when placed between a greenhouse and indoor living area. Single-pass filters can also be located to intercept particulates that derive from workshop processing and other activities and keep them from entering occupant areas.

Charcoal (Carbon) Filters

Where odor as well as gaseous contaminants might be in the indoor atmosphere, activated charcoal filters can be a preferred choice. Such filters, however, must be monitored and replaced on a timely basis to prevent unloading of the contaminants captured by the filter back into the airstream. The effectiveness of activated charcoal in removing gaseous contaminants varies with the type of pollutant, the concentration in the air, humidity and temperature, and the velocity through the filter. These filters are not very effective in removing formaldehyde, ammonia, carbon monoxide, or sulfur dioxide. Charcoal filters can be used in combination with any other type of filter media. They are available for both central and portable machines. Activated charcoal filters come in many sizes and types. Some are available within a cellular frame through which air passes and others with trays in which air passes over the charcoal.

Room-Type Air Cleaners

Room-type air-cleaning machines use various types of filtration systems. A multistage catalytic-type unit that can function at room temperature has the advantage of relatively high efficiency. This room temperature catalytic system has the ability to oxidize carbon monoxide to carbon dioxide, and also exhibits activity against many other toxic and noxious gases such as hydrogen cyanide, sulfur dioxide, oxides of nitrogen, ozone, methane, and butane, as well as many components of cigarette smoke. The catalyst has a high rate of activity over wide ranges of relative humidity and temperature. This effective unit combines the catalytic filter with a HEPA element and activated carbon. It cleans but, however, does not ionize the air.

HEPA filter units are a preferred choice in room-type machines. These filters have been tested and found to remove 99.97 percent of particulates at a size of 0.3 microns, and they maintain this efficiency over the life of the filter without production of ozone. They are effective in removing bacteria, pollen, viruses, and dust. HEPA filter systems in room conditioners have the drawback of higher noise levels due to greater filter media resistance and do not ionize the air unless so designed.

Portable Air Cleaners

Electronic portable units (preferred with activated charcoal filters) have lower filter media resistance and consequently tend to be quieter and have lower power demands. Some portable air cleaning units use negative ionization combined with various particle intercepting filters. These hybrid units may combine a prefilter, activated charcoal filter, and a HEPA filter or electrostatic precipitator.

Negative Ionization and Positive Field Resonance

Ionization plays a critical role in our fragile existence within the atmosphere. Negative ions are created by atmospheric electricity, lightning, waterfalls, in certain hill and mountain areas, and through the tips of pine needles. Negative ions stimulate our endocrine system in its production of hormones. Hormones are essential to our life processes. They are the internal messengers and control agents of our bodily functions. Negative ions can enhance human performance and increase metabolic activity and cellular growth at certain levels. Scientists suspect that the biological system is enhanced when ionized air molecules enter the bloodstream through the skin or by inhalation and then increase oxidation and removal of waste products in the body.

The air is cleaned to a substantive degree by negative ionization, in which the negatively charged particles (irritants and contaminants) are grounded off to the earth or other surfaces. Precipitation as rain, snow, or sleet aids the process of air purification. Trees, forests, grasses, and other vegetation not only provide oxygenation but also aid purification by means of ionization, texture, and filtration.

Negative ion generator units can remove small particles down to .001 microns. Because the negatively charged particles are free in the air, they will attach to the nearest grounding surface. Metal elements have a special affinity for such grounding (even the unseen nails used for drywall will accumulate unsightly dark residues). Thus special care needs to be exercised as to the distance (preferably over two feet) of the ionizer to any given wall or ceiling surface. A positive magnetic field plate strategically located will receive the dirt-laden ionized particles and lessen the probability of wall or ceiling soilage.

Negative ionization gives us a feeling of well-being, reduces air pollution, vitalizes indoor air, reduces the feeling of pain, heals burns, and suppresses bacterial growth. Negative ionization also stimulates plant growth. The exterior surfaces of homes and buildings ground off naturally occurring outdoor negative ionization, even window screens. Industrial fumes and automotive exhaust also deplete negative ions.

Within the indoor environment, negative ions are grounded out in the ductwork of forced-air mechanical heating and cooling systems (that act as a sink for negative ions), by exposed electric radiant heating elements, and by grounded electrical conduits, equipment, and metallic items. Most indoor pollutants also reduce ambient negative ions. Thus, positive ions tend to prevail and negative ions tend to be depleted within indoor space. Excess positive ions attach to carbon dioxide molecules, speeding up transfer of CO_2 into the bloodstream, which acts as a depressant to our biological system.

All microbes, viruses, and bacteria are negatively charged. The human body also has a net negative charge. Thus we have a natural protection from invasion by bacteria and viruses because of electrostatic repulsion (like charges repel). Negative ionization interferes with the net negative charge metabolism of these microorganisms, suppressing their growth.

Ion-generating equipment used indoors for air purification will perform with different levels of negative ion production. Inasmuch as a large output of negative ions will greatly stimulate our awareness level, they can interfere with sleep. Putting the unit on a timer to cut off during sleep periods can solve this problem. Ion generators that produce ozone should not be used. Electric baseboard heating should be the hydronic type to avoid the depletion of negative ions grounded out on conventional resistance heating elements.

Negative ionization improves the sweeping motion of bronchial cilia, with improved flow of mucus, that trap and sweep out foreign particulates from the respiratory system. In the case of polonium-210, the respiratory clearance is improved by about 20 percent, and particles, including those with harmful radioactivity, are swept into the digestive system where they are harmlessly expelled. Negative ionization improves respira-

199

tory response and airways function so that daytime and nocturnal breathing is enhanced.

Because the Earth's core is composed of molten iron, it has a negative ground plane. The ionosphere is positively charged due to cosmic energy bombardment. Between the Earth's surface and the ionosphere there exist natural resonant frequencies of 7.83, 14, 21, 28, and 32 cycles per second (Hertz). This phenomenon was discovered by W.O. Schumann in 1952. Humans evolved under these natural resonant frequencies. The Schumann resonance of 7.83 Hz coincides with alpha brain wave patterns. Buildings with metal framework or supports act as Faraday cages (including window screens) that shield out the natural Schumann resonance and leave indoor spaces devoid of this beneficial radiation. Inside most buildings the dominant environment is the 60 Hertz frequency of alternating current. Workers in a 60-Hz environment for an extended period can experience a drop in efficiency to as low as 30 percent of normal, according to University of Chicago studies.

The 7.83 Hz Schumann resonant field can be duplicated indoors with equipment that produces magnetic radiation within this narrow band. There are no standards for indoor ionization or electromagnetic fields, nor regulations or standards that preclude Hertzian or nonHertzian radiation that can be harmful to persons within its field. Low frequency ground waves also raise the question of relative biologic risk.

Electron Field Generator

An air-cleaning portable electron generator is available that generates and propagates negative electron fields that neutralize positively charged molecules on nonconductive indoor surfaces and positive charges on airborne pollutants. A stated description by the manufacturer of the electron generator is that it is designed to clean the air by a "cascade" effect of proliferating wave-form negative charges that combine with and neutralize the positive charges. Subsequently, by a subtle weight increase and gravity, and by slight negative charges sustained by the generator in their magnetic attraction to the floor, airborne particulates in principle drop to the floor and other surfaces where they may be readily cleaned up.

The electron field effect generator is designed for installation in an unconfined location (some with advised position) near the ceiling of an interior space. One unit is stated to cover approximately 2000 to 3000 square feet, with an average ceiling height not over 8 feet. These units tend to be relatively quiet with low velocity air movement and require no filters.

Described performance of the wave effect electron generator ascribed to the method includes: reduction of smoke, dust, suspended particulates, odor, and microorganisms and a reduction in static electricity from interior surfaces, with low maintenance and economy of operation.

The electron field effect generator, while producing negative field charges, should not be confused with negative ionizers and Schumann positive field resonance devices. The device has been used in commercial, industrial, and office environs that are subject to sources of smoke, particulates, and other airborne contaminants. The effectiveness of the electron generator and other air-cleaning equipment depends upon the conditions of indoor air as affected by ventilation, type of heating and cooling system, and occupant activities.

Absorption

Industrial plants use absorption processes, commonly referred to as scrubbing or air washing, to remove gaseous contaminants by passing contaminated air over wetted surfaces or through a liquid spray. These processes will remove only those pollutants that are soluble or chemically reactive to the liquid in use. Absorption processes are not currently available for residential applications.

Adsorption

Adsorbents are porous solid materials that trap pollutants by surface adhesion. Commonly used adsorbents include activated charcoal (mentioned above), silica gel, activated alumina, and molecular sieves. Adsorbents become saturated over time and must be regenerated or replaced.

Molecular adsorbers containing alkali alumina silicate/sodium or zeolites are available (in various appropriate sizes) for removal of a broad range of odors, vapors, mildew, and gases from indoor air. Zeolites are natural volcanic minerals that are capable of gas adsorption, water adsorption/desorption, and ion exchange. These molecular adsorbers have no moving parts and act as molecular sieves in removal of air contaminants.

Some of the gases adsorbed are: carbon dioxide, carbon monoxide, ethanol, ethane, chlorine, methanol, ethylene, propane, chloroform, carbon tetrachloride, benzene, hydrocarbons, sulfur dioxide, oil vapors, olefin, ammonia, formaldehyde, and others that can have adverse biologic effects. The scope of odors covers most of those we may encounter in our environs, including those from cigarettes. Adsorbent manufacturers claim their products are useful in reducing levels of airborne radon gas.

Activated charcoal is claimed to be an effective adsorber of ozone and the gaseous odors from a wide range of hydrocarbons, chemicals, solvents, esters, tobacco smoke, and microorganic activity. Activated charcoal adsorbs virtually all organic and many inorganic airborne odors. Concentration, humidity and temperature, velocity, and surface area of the charcoal are relevant to effectiveness of removal as an odorous gas passes through an activated carbon filter.

Permanganate is also an adsorbent that not only adsorbs gases, but also acts as an oxidizing agent. Other applications for permanganate include removal of hydrocarbons and carbon monoxide.

Clean Rooms

Various analytic and process needs require "clean rooms," where the indoor atmosphere must be free of airborne particles and often airborne gases, vapors, and aerosols that might be harmful to certain manufacturing and medical functions. Sensitive electronic and computer equipment requires a clean air environment. Delicate processes that can be reactive to airborne contaminants also often need a clean air environs.

HEPA filtration was developed to meet the exigencies of the "clean air" need. However, due to the production of particulates and electrostatic attraction around the person and his or her work space, these localized contaminants interfere with clean work station activities. In contrast, using HEPA filtration with negative ion production and positive pulse electro-field collection (7.83 Schumann resonance) removes the airborne contaminants from the work station area. A side benefit is the negative ionization of the air that is conducive to physiologic well-being and enhanced workplace performance.

This methodology of continuous electrophoresis effect (EpE) removes contaminants as small as 0.001 micron to as large as

100 microns. HEPA filtration alone fails to address all the contaminants, vapors, and aerosols that are generated within the turbulent clean room space. HEPA units typically filter particles about 0.2 microns or larger and are not effective for smaller particulates.

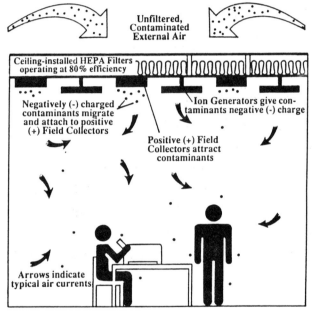

Cleanroom with EpE System and HEPA Filtration

In a cleanroom in which the continuous Electrophoresis Effect (EpE) System is installed, airborne contaminants as small as 0.001 micron to as large as 100 microns are electrically removed up and away from the work area.

An EpE system can be of particular benefit within medical and dental surgical rooms and in hospital wings and laboratories where infectious conditions may be present. The EpE suppression of harmful bacteria is consistent with sanitation and sterilization that should be paramount to medical and health facilities. Due to the vitalization of the air, a physiologic benefit is conferred to the physician, medical personnel, and the patient. Persons with environmental illness (EI) who are ultra-sensitive to airborne contaminants can also benefit from EpE systems.

The system consists of a negative ion source and positive field collectors. Typically both components are suspended from the ceiling in a grid pattern, with collectors and ion generators at 4-, 6-, or 8-foot intervals. Electrons from the ionizer are accepted by air molecules and are converted to air ions. These ions collide with airborne contaminants, and the negatively charged particles move through an electric field to the positive field collector (an electro-conductive carbon foam pad).

No noise originates from EpE negative ion and positive resonance field equipment, in contrast to mechanical means for air cleaning. A combination of HEPA filtration and an EpE system is particularly effective. But as HEPA systems require substantial horsepower for recirculation and ventilation air, measures should be taken to acoustically baffle and isolate-mount blower equipment.

The author has lived with an EpE system for 10 years. Located in the geographical center of Denver and subject to high pollution levels, the residence is often "buttoned up" during periods of protracted outdoor pollution. In contrast to the polluted outdoor air, the indoor air quality remains alive and vital. Persons coming in remark about the spring-like, fresh air quality.

Seasonal Effect on Indoor Air Cleaning

Residences are a notably different situation for indoor air filtration and ionization air-cleaning machines and devices than that commonly experienced in commercial buildings. Air changes per hour (ACH), the quality of outdoor intake air, the indoor factors of air contamination, and activities occurring within the space being conditioned have a performance effect upon central and room-type air-cleaning equipment.

Operable windows, patio doors, or air vents that directly receive outside ventilation air in residences and commercial buildings affect indoor air by the variant pollution and contaminants that accompany outdoor intake air. Indoor air systems used to clean the air can struggle against the influx of automotive fumes, dust, pollens, variant particulates, and chemical gases and odors present in the immediate area around the home or building. Commercial buildings that are completely sealed against the outdoor atmosphere and with variable "economizer" mechanical air handling systems should be evaluated as to appropriate air-cleaning options.

Due to seasonal temperature change, outdoor air ventilation of indoor spaces mostly occurs when temperatures are close to those acceptable for human comfort. When sunspaces intervene between outdoor intake air and indoor occupant spaces, solar air tempering can extend the occupant "comfort zone" for a longer seasonal period in cold climates. Filtering intake air used for ventilation is highly desirable to remove as many particulates as possible before the air enters indoor air-cleaning systems and devices. Contaminated outdoor ventilation air can compromise and clog indoor air filtration equipment and denigrate the performance of negative ionization systems.

At certain times of the year dust, airborne particles, and noxious gases and ozone can prevail. Recognizing this reality (and the performance of air-cleaning devices and equipment), appropriate filter changes should be performed at regular intervals.

When selecting air-cleaning systems, it is advisable to consider not only the internal requirements for the air volume and other internal conditions, but also the seasonal aspects of ventilation with its accompaniment of particulates, gases, and odors. Regardless of season, the best procedure is to remove all pollution sources from the outdoor and indoor spaces of a property. A qualified professional should be engaged as to the best selection of natural and mechanical ventilation and air-cleaning systems relative to specific conditions that exist.

Vacuum Cleaners

Not to be neglected are vacuum cleaners that are used for cleaning carpet, other floor coverings, upholstery, drapes, and household fabrics. Most upright or tank-type vacuum cleaning machines have filters that do <u>not</u> adequately filter out the dust, mold, spores, mites, and other contaminants present in carpets and on interior surfaces.

Two types of portable residential vacuum cleaners are available that offer better than average performance. One type uses a combination of HEPA and activated charcoal filters with extra-powerful suction and a 14-layer cellulose filter bag. It approximates a portable room air cleaner and captures particles down to 0.3 microns. Another type uses water as the filter medium, and variations of it have been on the market for many years. This vacuum is also reputed to intercept particles as small as 0.3 microns. Floors cleaned of household contaminants remove a substantial cleaning burden from room air-cleaning equipment.

Central vacuum systems are available that have the benefit of removing room dirt and conveying it to remote canisters, and they avoid the recontamination factor of most ordinary vacuum cleaners.

Summary

Efficiency claims can be deceptive for all types of air-cleaning machines. There are no standardized national rating systems or unified testing requirements. The filter medium and its relationship to the particles, gaseous pollutants, or micro-organisms to be removed and its performance in doing so are critical to choice.

All of the filter systems use a fan or squirrel cage blower, except for negative ionizers that are designed to operate on the basis of electrical charges without forced air movement. In general, as the efficiency of the filtering unit is improved by more effective filters, the noise of the unit in operation is likely to become less tolerable. Electrostatic units are subject to cracking noises from particles that cross the electrostatic grid and by sparking create ozone.

For the most part, portable room-type air-cleaning machines are available with more sophisticated filtering means (such as the catalytic room temperature type) than those available for central forced-air systems. But in the near future more effective units are likely to become available for centralized systems.

Filters should be dutifully changed or cleaned (for cleanable types) when they start to lose their effectiveness or begin to unload the contaminants they pick up from the airstream. Replaceable filters can be relatively expensive. Cleanable filters (such as electrostatic) and a non-filter portable unit (such as a negative ion generator) avoid such cost. Electrostatic and tray-type charcoal filters (located downstream) are available for most forced-air systems. HEPA or other dense filters that retard air movement should <u>not</u> be used if there is danger of overloading the capacity of the fan or blower.

As to cleaning up the indoor air of any home, workplace, or other indoor environment, a number of factors need to be considered:

a. outdoor sources of air pollutants
b. location of intake air for indoor ventilation
c. indoor sources of air pollutants
d. total daily and seasonal outdoor and indoor air pollutants
e. amount of outdoor air needed for indoor oxygenation and ventilation
f. location of exterior openings for indoor ventilation
g. location of exterior openings, stacks, or mechanical means for venting indoor air
h. indoor time of day activities and rest requiring rates of ventilation
i. central or portable systems for air cleaning
j. systems most suited re: type and adequacy for concentration of pollutants
k. noise of operation of air-cleaning devices or equipment
l. performance data of specific air-cleaning devices or equipment
m. operational costs including filter replacement

n. location of air-cleaning devices and equipment for effective performance

o. judgment as to when to ventilate with outdoor air and when to operate devices or equipment.

Ventilation can often be a more appropriate, cost-effective measure using outdoor make-up air, particularly with the extenuating difficulty in adequately filtering cigarette smoke.

A host of air-cleaning devices and machines are appearing on the market as consumers become increasingly aware of indoor air pollution. Many of the units combine filtration systems. Some use prefilters, HEPA or other filters with above-average filtering ability, and sometimes with negative ionization as a final stage. In principle those that provide a negative ionizing final stage can vitalize the air commensurate with biologic sensitivities and well-being. Inasmuch as sequential filtering will to a considerable extent remove particulates, the problem of soilage of indoor surfaces should be negligible or eliminated.

Manufacturers prescribe certain room sizes, areas, or air volumes compatible with their equipment. But in actual performance under existing environmental conditions they may not be adequate. Testing of equipment within actual conditions is advised.

Electrostatic equipment with downstream activated charcoal filtration is commonly used to capture the contaminants of tobacco smoke. Frequent washing of the electrostatic filter is essential and less costly than the frequent replacement necessary with HEPA or other disposable-type filters. Charcoal filters should be promptly replaced when their adsorption level no longer remains effective. Cocktail lounges and other places where smoke-laden air is likely to prevail can benefit by electrostatic air cleaning and engineered exhaust systems.

While primary measures should be first taken to control and reduce indoor radon to an acceptable level, electrostatic air cleaning is purported to be an effective secondary way to reduce ambient radon levels. Engineering research indicates that electrostatic air cleaners may remove up to 70% of attached and 15% of unattached radon decay products in indoor air. However, the air-cleaning performance is dependent upon particle concentration, air flow patterns and velocity, turbulence, humidity, and interior surface materials and ductwork where particles may deposit.

CURTAILING WASTE AND AIR POLLUTION

All waste translates into increments of air pollution. And all outdoor air pollution is an increment of indoor air pollution.

Wasteful technology, transport, and habits all represent an amount of air pollution. The inefficiencies of our petro-fueled vehicles, our industry, our homes, buildings, and energy networks all result in amounts of air pollution.

Waste begins with how we conceive, plan, and design. Waste keeps extending as we inefficiently or ineffectually employ energy and resources with what we design, manufacture, or otherwise bring into being.

We are the most wasteful of nations. Our per capita consumption of energy, products, and resources has no equal. Our American dream of "more" per capita affluence translates into unparalleled denigration of our global air. We are literally at war with our environment and the vitality of our global atmosphere and with our own health and vitality within indoor spaces. There are some pressures on industry to produce more energy-efficient products and for the housing industry to conserve energy. But in the main there is no "cap" on the amount of petro-energy or proliferate use of materials, methods, and distribution to reasonably limit inefficiency and waste that accompany diverse industries.

214

The places where we work, shop, dine, learn, or play have less than optimal efficiency of architecture and systems. Banks of fluorescent lights vastly exceed visual and task needs as daylight prevails. Mechanical systems are often inefficiently designed. By lack of concern and habit, we waste energy and generate air pollution.

The crux of our outdoor and indoor atmospheric problems is the incessant media stimulation of desire and expectation. There is no per capita limit on the petro-energies or other atmospheric-degrading energies we use, on the size of homes we live in, or on the number or kind of possessions we have that pollute the indoor spaces of our architecture or undermine the local and global atmosphere.

Every choice and use of what we have has a direct or indirect effect upon the air we breathe. How many miles we drive; the efficiency of our car, our home, and the products we buy and use; and the waste that results from initial and ongoing petro-chemical, toxic, or nuclear energy demands add up in measure to a personal impact upon the outdoor and indoor vitality of air.

It is not just a matter of choice of products but also the energy intensities, distance, and processing required from basic source to point of use. All foreign products bear the disadvantage of atmospheric pollution in their distance from resources to ultimate destination in another country. The more we can provide per capita needs without this global waste and denigration by *in situ* and localized use of sun, air, earth, and water energies and point-of-use efficiency, the more will be our preservation of global atmospheric protection, regenerative capability, and purity and vitality of breathable air.

It is not only the product but also the packaging and means of distribution and delivery (such as air flight delivery that is more polluting than by rail). Diesel truck fumes are particularly noxious on the highway and to our atmosphere. The kind and amount of waste that is produced are also relevant to atmospheric pollution. Recycling is a great virtue, but abstinence from products that are energy intensive, nonbiodegradable, and emit toxins or radioactivity on disposal can well be a personal ethic. Unless we address the "pollution trail" from initial source to final use or disposal, we remain remiss in our view of air quality consequences.

Waste has become so overwhelming that it is one of our greatest municipal problems. The question, "Where to put it?" needs to be answered. First is how <u>not</u> to create it. Secondly, what are the nonpolluting alternatives? Thirdly, how can we efficiently (with minimal attendant pollution) reuse or recycle it?

Some municipalities are shipping their waste 500 miles or more as their landfills or other means of disposal become inadequate. Economically desperate underdeveloped nations often accept rubbish and toxic waste from developed nations that can no longer find a safe or adequate place for disposal within their own territory. The ever-mounting and inexorable waste of our techno-societies is neglected as underdeveloped nations seek to emulate our technology and lifestyle.

The EPA estimates that one-third of our nation's landfills will be at capacity within two years. Approximately 80 percent of our waste goes into landfills. About 11 percent is recycled and 9 percent incinerated. The EPA is strongly encouraging recycling and would like to see an expeditious reduction in landfill disposal of more than 50 percent.

Imaginative and constructive new perceptions are needed to maximize all waste as a resource. But the initial emphasis should be on imaginative and constructive first-place alternatives to avoid the ultimate and ever-incessant overload of waste that issues from our techno-society. Efficiency of systems and responsible elimination or optimal curtailing of waste are critical to minimizing air pollution and atmospheric harm. Our nation needs to become a model of ecologic concern and action. The "American Dream" of expectation and prosperity is drowning in a sea of waste.

It is impossible to divorce the air that we breathe indoors from that of the global atmosphere. It is equally impossible to divorce global air quality from our individual and collective thinking and actions.

We cannot continue to use the atmosphere as a sewer without expecting substantial and potentially irreversible global disruption.

-- Stephen Schneider, scientist
National Center for Atmospheric Research

THE REALITY

Within the multi-level impacts we impose upon our local, global, and indoor atmosphere, we hold the key to cleaner air and life-sustaining values.

+ Global control over global air quality is essential for health and existence of the world's populations.

+ Our oil- and coal-based dependence and economy will reach an ultimate crisis in less than 25 years.

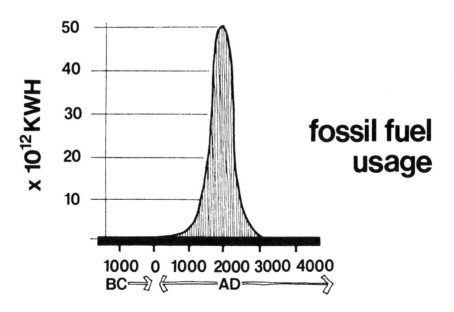

219

+ Nuclear fission power generation is defunct practically, economically, and in its momentous burden of long-term radioactive waste. Nuclear fusion <u>might</u> become a less hazardous reality.

+ Loss of protective stratospheric ozone is a grim reality.

+ Nuclear sabotage, accident, or terroristic or dissident happenings can trigger the ultimate extinction of humanity.

+ Our breathable air for sustainable human vitality and health is declining.

+ We are in a conceptual, social, energy, resource, and institutional revolution of world-scale magnitude. Human survival hangs on it.

+ Only a new conceptual holistic design, a developmental realization, systemic reordering, and economic redeployment of effort, energy, and resources can stem the denigration of our world and national environment.

+ Only by being in phase with Nature and to conceptually and resolutely optimize our use of sun, air, earth, and water energies and maximize regenerative, ecologic, and biologic sustainability can we survive.

+ The stop-gap measures and panaceas that we employ to stem the erosion of our vitality and health at the localized level are only an interim solution.

+ The indoor and outdoor atmosphere is that in which we live, work, and play. We should be its most devoted guardians.

+ We need to stop the use of pesticides, use safe "organic" agricultural practices, and with great caution use biologic and entomological controls.

+ Government standards, regulations, and punitive taxation are needed to control all products, materials, and substances harmful to health or environmental quality.

+ Reducing car mileage in favor of phoning, walking, bicycle riding, and written correspondence will reduce air pollution.

+ Waste is a valuable resource, and it should be constructively utilized in a manner that avoids air pollution.

+ Wilderness, park lands, and ecologically sound landscaping are fundamental to viable air quality.

+ We need environmental protection of phytoplankton of our coastal waterways and oceans that are a primary source of the world's oxygen.

+ We need to preserve our global tropical, national, and other forests and actively concentrate on forest regeneration and massive tree planting efforts.

+ If we believe in the continuance of the human species, we cannot rely on gradualistic change to save us from our present narrow, short-term concepts and institutionalizations.

+ International concern and cooperation are essential to meet the magnitude of global atmospheric problems.

+ International incentives are critical to effectively study, evaluate, and motivate appropriate and expeditious remedial action.

+ Nondenigrating resources, nonpolluting energy, and ecologic equity and justice are principal to international harmony and atmospheric vitalization.

OUR LARGER RESPONSIBILITY

Indoor air quality has both local and global implications.
On the local scene, people live, work, and play within indoor spaces that are beset with poisonous contaminants, harmful particulates, and injurious radioactivity.

On a global scale, the atmosphere is seriously polluted by fossil-fueled industrialization and transportation and by people engaged in activities contrary to Nature. Air pollution is energy related. The more we use fossil fuels, the worse air pollution gets. Outdoor air is the source of the indoor air we breathe.

We unwisely power our vehicles, industry, and many homes and buildings with gasoline, oil, or coal; use toxic chemicals; make equipment and products that outgas harmful contaminants; and use materials that give off dangerous particles or radioactivity. Our short range view provokes intense adverse biologic consequences. With five percent of the world's population, we consume 10 times the global average of energy (with its global atmospheric pollution).

At home and abroad we need to relieve and abate all causes of air quality deprecation. It is a critical matter of health and survival.

REMEDIAL POSITION

To reduce our injury to the Earth's global atmosphere, drastic changes are essential in our technologic lifestyles. Air pollution (outdoors and indoors) attends every moment of our way of life, our choices, and our activities. Other facets of technology and lifestyle also threaten global habitability.

A public consciousness is developing about the conditions and fate of the global environment. A "public attitude" and crusading commitment might hopefully develop to lessen impending, adverse, irreversible changes to the global climate.

Massive reforestation, "clean" fuels for vehicles and industry, science and technology responsibly aligned with natural ecosystems and ecosystemic viability, industrial restructuring to eliminate deprecation of the atmosphere, and public policies and action fully committed to ecologic vitality and ecosystemic integrity are principal remedial means.

We are all part and parcel of Nature's ecosystems. And we are part and parcel of a technologic lifestyle that undermines Nature's vitality. **As we are individually and collectively the "cause," we can become the "redeemer" of Nature's ecology and ecosystemic vitality**. Our global atmosphere is at peril. The local atmosphere that provides the indoor air of our homes and buildings must of necessity be breathable. Our "American dream" of technologic inventions needs to be restated as an <u>ecologic vision</u> of science and technology with an ethic that does not deplete Nature.

Our techno-society has been an unfortunate model for the rest of the world. As nations aspire to our "standard of living," the global atmosphere is more imperiled. Until global petrochemical energies, toxic chemistry, and adverse radiative fields are abandoned in favor of "safe and clean" nonpolluting, non-denigrating, oxygen-restoring sources, our global future will remain in critical jeopardy.

The seemingly "short" cuts always mean danger to mankind. As soon as glad tidings of the "short" cut are heard, mankind leaves its path and the way is lost.

-- Nietzsche

APPENDIX

Our Global Atmosphere

Our global atmosphere is suffering. Our technologic lifestyles, growing population, industry, fossil fuels use, and sociologic and economic inequities are rapidly degrading our global atmosphere. The dire result is evidenced in "greenhouse effect" global warming, depletion of the "ozone layer," the spreading of "acid rain," and heavy pollution that shrouds our cities.

How we condition indoor air and live our lives affect the quality of the global atmosphere. As the global atmosphere becomes more polluted, indoor air becomes less breathable.

The "Greenhouse Effect"

Scientific opinions vary as to the magnitude and kind of climatic changes that may result from "global warming." Drastic changes are predicted that could render areas of our planet much hotter or colder than experienced in the past.

Global warming of the atmosphere is caused by the stratification of mainly carbon dioxide, methane, and nitrous oxide. The stratified layer allows penetration of solar radiation but acts as a reflective boundary to re-radiation from the earth.

227

The net result is a corresponding increase in global temperature. However, while some predict and foretell a heating up of northern latitudes, others perceive a global heating up of the tropics and the possibility of an arctic-advancing global ice age. These dire predictions have a basis in the reality of our technologic mutilation of Nature's ecosystemic integrity. The United States is responsible for about one-fifth of the world's CO_2 emissions, and 98 percent of these come from fossil fuel burning.

"Greenhouse effect" global warming results from multi-leveled causes. International cooperation as well as local and national efforts are critical to reduce and alleviate carbon dioxide levels and other sources of atmospheric harm. Researchers estimate that a 50 percent reduction in carbon dioxide emissions will eventually be necessary to stabilize atmospheric carbon dioxide. Strategies to achieve such a reduction include using natural gas in place of coal and oil, using energy more efficiently, switching to renewable energy sources, and reversing global deforestation.

The Ozone Layer

Ozone, a pollutant at ground level, makes life on Earth possible by filtering the sun's ultraviolet rays 15 to 25 miles up. Recent findings of arctic research by the Jet Propulsion Laboratories of Pasadena, California, indicate how chlorofluorocarbons (CFCs) destroy the ozone layer. They report that chlorine atoms from fluorocarbons react with ozone molecules to form chlorine monoxide (ClO). These molecules combine respectively with other ClO molecules to form dimers (pairs of identical molecules). The dimers then break apart, liberating two free chlorine atoms that begin this process over again. In this cycle more and more ozone is destroyed. This perpetuating process is only halted by the next influx of fresh ozone.

As the ozone layer becomes thinner, an increase in the penetration of ultraviolet radiation can lead to greater incidence of skin cancer. Other consequences of increased ultraviolet radiation could be alteration of climatic cycles and serious effects upon crop production.

An elimination or substitution of CFCs for various products and activities, such as Freon used for refrigerated cooling of architecture or vehicles, cleaning of electronic and other parts, for automotive and other finishes, for foamed insulation, packing, and other items, for fire-extinguishing halons, and in some countries as a propellant, is being examined on a national and international basis. Voluntary reduction and cessation over time has been claimed as a policy by major manufacturers of CFCs. As we avoid using CFCs, we help the cause of atmospheric protection.

Acid Rain

Sulfurous emissions from coal-burning power plants and automotive vehicles become acidic in the atmosphere and imperil forests, lakes, and life within them. The emissions travel far and wide and decimate fragile ecosystems. They can have an erosive effect upon the exterior surface of architecture. Fish, wildlife, and natural organisms of the soil do not survive when the acidic concentration reaches a deadly level.

Alternative technologies for power production; solar, photo-voltaic, and thermal-concentrating fields; wind energy; geothermal energy; tidal power; alternative clean fuels for motor vehicles; architecture that optimizes site-specific energies of sun, air, earth, and water; and "fluid bed" and anti-acidic technologies for power plants can bring about a reduction in acid rain levels.

Electromagnetic Energies (surrounding an electrically charged object)

Electric fields - such as those produced by electrical devices, television screens, electrical systems, and appliances in the home and workplace. (charged particles in motion)

Magnetic fields - power line magnetic fields have been associated with cancer, neural disorders, weakening of the immune system, general malaise, dysfunction, and birth defects.

Electromagnetic radiation - Electromagnetic radiation covers a broad range of frequencies in the form of ionizing radiation and non-ionizing radiation. Ionizing radiation is exemplified by ultraviolet (UV-C) light, X-rays, gamma radiation, and cosmic rays. Non-ionizing radiation includes ultraviolet light (UV-A and UV-B), visible light (spectral color range), infrared light (perceived as radiant heat), microwaves (in the centimeter and millimeter range), radio and TV broadcast waves (1 meter to 10 kilometers), and extremely low and ultra-low frequencies that complete the electromagnetic spectrum.

Ionizing radiation harms us by direct mutation of the DNA molecule.

Non-ionizing radiation covers two categories of effects. They are identified as thermal effects in which a rise in temperature of at least 1/10 of a degree Celsius is evident. Non-thermal effects are associated with exposure to non-ionizing radiation with intensity levels that produce less than a 1/10 degree Celsius change. Generally no temperature change is evident. Non-thermal effects are observed principally in living systems. Thermal intensities are harmful because the radiation amplitude is sufficient to cause a moderate increase in temperature.

Almost instantaneous biologic dysfunction or death can result from intense microwave exposure, such as inside an operating

231

microwave oven or within several feet of an operating radar-transmitting antenna.

The biological effects of both non-ionizing frequencies and non-thermal levels of these frequencies are much debated within scientific literature. The preponderance of evidence of the last decade strongly suggests that non-thermal levels of non-ionizing radiation frequencies from extra low frequency (ELF) to ultraviolet B (UV-B) do have biological effects, some beneficial, some harmful. An example of non-thermal effects (scientifically debated) are the possible harmful effects from high-voltage power lines.

Numerous studies suggest that living or working near high-voltage power lines for extended periods of time is associated with observable effects of biologic harm, including an increase in cancer, deprecation of the immune system, other disorders, and increased cases of depression and suicide.

Electromagnetic Precautions

Within the urban environment it is not uncommon to find a 1 milligauss (100 nanoTeslas) or higher level of electromagnetic field in homes and buildings. Three milligauss or greater appears to be an electromagnetic threshold at or beyond which cancer or other biologic anomalies are more likely to occur. Dr. Robert O. Becker in his book Cross Currents holds to this premise and further states that using a safety factor of

232

ten, a 0.3 milligauss field can be regarded as reasonably safe. European researchers hold to a corresponding view.

Nancy Wertheimer, an epidemiologist who initially raised the question of electromagnetic fields from power lines as a probable cause of cancer in children, and Ed Leeper, a physicist who works with the assessment of power line fields, question the effect of sustained electromagnetic fields above 1 milligauss.

In the course of evolution, our "body electric" was designed to correspond to the prevailing low-frequency field of the Schumann resonance, a positive pulse field between the earth and ionosphere. But we live in a "technologic indoor world" of inescapable anti-biologic electrical frequencies in which propitious Schumann fields are mainly excluded by the Faraday cage effect of the architectural enclosure. We need to take into account the dangerous possibilities of 60-cycle electrical circuits of electric lighting, appliances, televisions, computers, and other devices in our homes and buildings and judge our proximity and exposure time to their relative electromagnetic fields. In addition, power line and other potentially harmful fields can penetrate us from external sources.

Very near the source, 60-Hertz milligauss field levels of various electrical appliances and devices, such as those listed below, can be extremely high. Within a customary proximity of our body from the electromagnetic source, the magnetic field intensity is most likely to exceed 1 milligauss.

electric clocks
electric blankets (whole body exposure)
electric hair dryers
electric shavers
fluorescent lamps and ceiling fixtures
electric radiant heaters and floor or ceiling systems
halogen lamp transformers
television sets
waterbed heaters
refrigerators
electric ranges
microwave ovens
computers

Relative exposure time is important to biologic impact as well as proximity to the source of the magnetic field. Whereas most appliances and other electrical items during operation generate fields of constant frequency and intensity, utility power lines, transformers, and some other devices emanate fluctuating fields due to varying power demands. Time-of-day electric usage from a number of utility customers has a direct magnetic influence on the utility line. The more the electric demand, the greater the magnetic field.

The fields from most electrical lighting and other electrical items within indoor space for the most part drop off rapidly within a short distance. A magnetic field of over 10 milligauss can drop to under 1 milligauss within several feet. But because of the length of a power line, the field does not fall off as rapidly. Thus the intensity of the field does not lessen to such a notable degree as with indoor point (or dipole) source wire coils that accompany lighting fixtures and other electric devices. Other localized fields from sources in the building you occupy contribute to a person's total level of exposure. Concern should be given to the penetration of magnetic fields through partitions or through floors or ceilings.

Household and building plumbing plays a role in the conveyance of electric currents through the architecture. A dielectric union between the plumbing and the utility water main can interrupt, lessen, or eliminate these currents to the water main and an element of undesired magnetic field and its effect upon interior space and people. An electrician should create a "ground" for the electrical circuitry of the building independent of the water lines. However, for safety in the event of a voltage surge or electrical fault, the power neutral as required by electrical codes should remain grounded to the plumbing system.

It is interesting to note that the median electromagnetic field of New York City is around 1 milligauss, but that in more remote places it can be relatively nil. Countryside places tend to have low to very low prevailing levels of electromagnetic fields.

Epidemiological evidence is suggestive that electromagnetic fields can lower the human immune response, which may promote the incidence or growth of certain cancers or may lead to neurological disorders. On the other side of the coin, electrotherapy is being used for bone healing and growth. The electromagnetic fields of TENS (transcutaneous electrical neural stimulation) units relieve about 60 percent of the cases of pain. Electromedicine is coming to the fore. A prime question is how we may use frequencies and intensities of current that are most conducive to the electromagnetic and electrolytic vitalities of our body. Avoiding the discrete "windows" of frequencies and field strengths that can do us harm requires precise information as to these "points" of the electromagnetic spectrum. To make such exact determinations as to biologic effect is no small task, considering the vast scope of the electromagnetic spectrum. But some headway is being made, and a scientific awareness is developing to this necessity.

Prudence is our best protection. An attempt to keep exposures to all 60-cycle AC fields under 1 milligauss (100 nanoTeslas) is prudent. Using a safety factor of 0.3 milligauss is most prudent. Possessing a meter that reads 60-cycle AC electromagnetic fields in milligauss or nanoTeslas is a good investment. It becomes easy to determine the magnetic field strength to which you can more safely be exposed. This applies to the multifarious electrical items we have in our homes and buildings, including light fixtures and their lamps. Kitchens with electrical appliances are particularly beset with fields that can be antagonistic to our wellness. The length of time we may be in any intense field should be a basic concern.

To be "safe" from commercial TV and FM towers, Dr. Becker advises that people should reside or work at least one-half mile from the tower. However, the signal can be blocked by a hill or tall building. Bioelectromagnetic concerns are a topic of increasing public awareness and debate.

In a society laden with electrical, electronic, and computer technologies, in our daily lives we are likely to be simultaneously exposed to a number of electromagnetic fields of varying frequencies and intensities. The total coincidence of more than one electromagnetic source adds to the consequence of exposure. In design and product manufacture, shielding (or other alternatives) is imperative to provide safety from potentially harmful electromagnetic fields.

Sunspace Design

Sunspaces can be of any type, size, or shape. Their types include indoor solar atria, galleries, greenhouses, sun rooms, and sunspaces. They should be located "true" solar south for effectiveness and with a not greater than 15° deviation from true south.

Sunspaces should be designed in accord with the sun's seasonal path and seasonal position at high noon. Direct solar collection for wintertime heating is effectual from 9 a.m. to 3 p.m. Clear double glazing to the south with no (or minimal) framing members that cast shadows is advised.

Atria are larger centralized spaces that can serve interior use. They are associated principally with commercial buildings, often acting as a central concourse to occupant spaces. Large glazed areas of the roof often predominate. While they do create a separation from the climate and have a delightful correspondence to the sky, when heated in winter atria lose much thermal energy to clear sky temperatures and the outdoor ambient temperature. They can overheat with direct solar radiation during warm and hot weather.

Large areas of roof glazing, skylights, and sloped glazing lose thermal energy as aforementioned, can drastically overheat, require safety glazing, are prone to leaks from rain and snow, and are receptors of outdoor airborne dust, dirt, and leaves. The glazing can become weather etched and it requires constant maintenance.

Thus for all of the diverse sunspace and greenhouse "packages" on the market, a simple vertical (or nearly so) design for glazing to the south with a well-insulated roof or upper floor over it is most economic, least troublesome, most effective for space use without roof solar radiation control methods, and of greatest benefit to people, plants, and furnishings. A roof overhang can provide summer shading, and using vertical blinds that require minimal space can provide desired solar control and privacy.

Ventilation should not be neglected. It should be adequate to match with seasonal conditions. Bringing in outdoor air low and exhausting the solar thermal gains as may be expedient by means of a roof stack that uses inductive, venturi, or cross ventilation or powered exhaust (that can operate on photovoltaic cells) is essential. Depending upon the architecture and its occupant spaces, various methods to internally use the solar sunspace heat for thermal gain, air tempering, and inductive ventilation can be employed.

A separation between the sunspace and the general living spaces of a homes or building is desirable. A glazed separation (with glazed door[s]) that can admit daylight, air from the sunspace, and provide access to it can benefit the interior with secondary direct or indirect solar gains in cool and cold weather.

Every project and the contemplated use of space, solar heat, air tempering, ventilation, and inductive thermal cooling are individualistic. Location, latitude, architecture, and the disposition of indoor occupant functions and whether the sunspace might have any, some, or a lot of vegetative planting, have a spa pool as a climatic buffer to the interior, and act as a source of daylighting are all germane to sunspace design and its relative location to interior and possible outdoor functions. Just sticking a greenhouse, sunspace, or conventional sun room on an existing home or incorporation into the plans of a new home is not advised without professional experience and judgment. While some benefit might accrue from a poorly conceived and designed sunspace, a well-designed and appropriately furnished sunspace is the most rewarding option.

Fundamental conceptual principles for the most effective use of sunspace solar gain and for interior daylighting relate to thermal mass and a converse principle of as rapidly as possible converting solar radiation to heated air. Every sunspace is a literal air-type solar collector. Thermal mass appropriate in color, size, and location for the reception of direct and indirect solar radiation is relative to heat retention and physical comfort. The thermal mass can be masonry, concrete, tile, eutectic salts (phase change materials), or water (colored dark or in a dark container). Location can be floor, walls, pylons, and ceilings where solar reflection is directed to it. Remote or centralized thermal mass storage for solar thermal air transfer systems should be designed to avoid the intrusion of radon and avoid gravel or masonry that exhibits radioactivity.

In contrast, intercepting dark-colored metal blinds (vertical or horizontal) or other dark metal or other surfaces can instantaneously convert shorter wavelength solar photon radiation to longer wavelength thermal (infrared) radiation to heat the air. Then by inductive convection and/or ductwork with a photovoltaically powered blower, the solar-heated air can be relocated to where it most effectively serves interior purposes. This solar air transfer principle is being investigated by Dr. Ren Anderson of the Solar Energy Research Institute. His calculations indicate as much as 50% of the energy can be saved over that of a thermal mass system located near the south glazing. Thermal mass reradiant losses to the outdoors during cold weather are greatly reduced.

The author has designed a number of completed projects using this latter principle during a period of 10 years. Overheating of the sunspace is largely avoided with the redistribution of the solar heat to internal thermal mass gravel storage beds between masonry walls, eutectic salt chambers, or other concentrated thermal mass. Air flow back as a return to the sunspace can be through occupied spaces as appropriate or by return air ductwork. The solar heat can be used as desired to provide floor slab heating, to heat interior spaces remote from the sunspace, and for thermal mass locations that favor comfort and reduce energy loss.

A judicious combination of solar air transfer and thermal mass considering year-round microclimatic solar access, thermal comfort, and effective solar thermal use is usually the best option. Every project should be conceptualized, designed, and implemented in the light of total (holistic) factors.

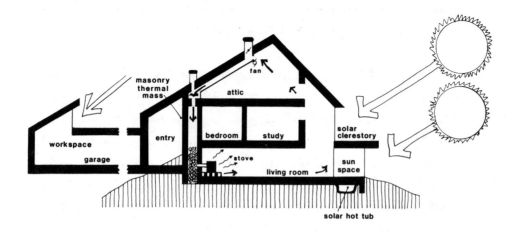

SOLAR HYBRID SYSTEM (1983 Residence)

Solar hybrid sunspace functions for cold weather heating, interseasonal air tempering, inductive ventilation, and attendant cooling. A thermostatically controlled blower transfers the passive solar heat gains from the sunspace, south-facing windows above the sunspace, and internal heat gains into the gravel-filled cavity between masonry walls. The flue of an energy-conserving stove also passes through the cavity to utilize its portion of waste heat. Aperture at the bottom of the wall allows the circulated air to return to the sunspace where it is reheated by the sun.

242

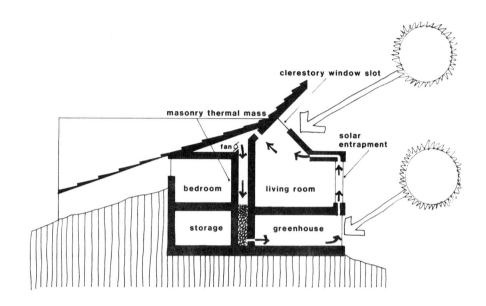

SOLAR HYBRID SYSTEM (1984 Residence)

A lower-level greenhouse with floor apertures into a narrow sunspace that acts like a heat transfer solar collector provide heat through ductwork and blower to a central thermal mass masonry gravel-filled cavity wall. Apertures at the bottom level of the wall allow for the air to be returned to the greenhouse and consequently to the sunspace and/or another completed circuit of solar-heated air. An energy-conserving circulating air fireplace with glass doors and outdoor combustion air intake is incorporated into the central masonry wall system, thus adding to the heat gain of the thermal mass.

243

Biospheric Systems

As an extension of the greenhouse concept, researchers in Arizona are currently readying a 2.5-acre completely closed ecosystem called "Biosphere II" for a two-year experiment to begin in 1990. Eight individuals will inhabit the biosphere that is designed to be a totally self-sufficient ecosystem where everything essential for life is recycled and regenerated. Eventually such a closed system could be used in heavily polluted urban areas for people who feel they have to live and work in such locations.

Depending upon the interior spatial volume and number and activity of the occupants, during days of high outdoor air pollution indoor spaces can be "closed up" and air be internally recycled and purified in an environment of negative ionization and positive field resonance. Concentrations of toxic gases and other indoor air pollutants would remain controlled at a safe level, and life could go on unhampered by high levels of outdoor air pollution.

<u>Carpet Cleaning</u>

For many years wall-to-wall carpeting has been a prevailing choice for homes and buildings. It lessens cleaning maintenance, provides a soft and pleasant surface to walk on, and has good acoustical properties. The principal drawback of broadloom carpeting has been the chemical constituents of its face and backing. And also, the use of chemicals to make stain removal easier and to kill bacteria can contribute irritating and toxic outgassing to indoor environments.

When cleaning carpet (beyond ordinary vacuuming) professionals use various chemicals in the process, which may or may not remain in the carpeting and have a possible adverse biologic effect. Rugs not secured to the floor can be sent out for cleaning. Within the home or workplace, the respiratory effect upon sensitive individuals (and everyone else) often remains obscure.

Processes that heavily wet the carpet can lead to or increase mildew. However, some carpet cleaning companies try to reduce the drying time while adequately cleaning the carpet. Chemical carpet cleaning processes that require little water are required to disclose toxic ingredients as defined by the EPA. However, some "nonhazardous" processes may affect certain sensitive persons. While carpeting as a possible causative agent of bioharmful outgassing is not recommended, it is the most prevalent floor covering in homes

245

and buildings. Manufacturers of carpeting should be required to use only nontoxic and nonallergenic materials.

Asbestos-Containing Materials and Abatement Methods

The following material is taken from an EPA publication, the 1985 edition of Guidance for Controlling Asbestos-Containing Materials in Buildings.

Three forms of asbestos are typically found in buildings: (1) sprayed- or troweled-on surfacing materials; (2) insulation on pipes, boilers, and ducts; and (3) miscellaneous forms, such as wallboard, ceiling tiles, and floor tiles. EPA surveys estimate that 31,000 schools and 733,000 public and commercial buildings contain friable (easily crumbled) asbestos-containing materials. Friable asbestos and asbestos disturbed during maintenance, repair, or renovation are of greatest concern from an exposure perspective.

Estimates indicate that only a small proportion of people exposed to low levels of asbestos will develop asbestos-related diseases. However, combining smoking with occupational exposure to asbestos increases the lung cancer rate above the rate due to either smoking or asbestos exposure alone. Also, asbestos exposure in children is of special concern: since they have a greater remaining lifespan than adults, their lifetime risk of developing mesothelioma (a rare cancer of the chest and abdominal lining) is greater. Avoiding unnecessary exposure to asbestos is prudent.

Asbestos-Containing Materials Found in Buildings

Surfacing material	sprayed- or troweled-on
Preformed thermal insulating products	batts, blocks, and pipe covering 85% magnesia calcium silicate
Textiles	cloth, blankets (fire), felts, sheets, cord/rope/yarn, tape, theater curtains
Cementitious concrete-like products	extrusion panels: corrugated, flat, flexible, roof tiles, clapboard, siding shingles, roofing shingles; pipe
Paper products	corrugated, indented, millboard
Roofing felts	smooth surface, mineral surface
Asbestos-containing compounds	caulking putties, adhesive (cold applied), joint compound, roofing asphalt, mastics, asphalt tile cement, roof putty, plaster/stucco, spackles
Flooring tile and sheet goods	vinyl/asbestos tile, asphalt/asbestos tile, sheet goods/resilient tile
Wallcovering	vinyl wallpaper
Paints and coatings	roof coating, air tight

Comparison of Asbestos Abatement Methods for Surfacing Materials

Method	Advantages	Disadvantages
Removal	Eliminates asbestos source	Replacement with substitute material may be necessary
	Eliminates need for special operations and maintenance program	Porous surfaces may also require encapsulation
Enclosure	Reduces exposure in area outside enclosure	Asbestos source remains and must be removed eventually
	Initial costs may be lower than for removal unless utilities need relocating or major changes	Fiber release continues behind enclosure
	Usually does not require replacement of material	Special operations program required to control access to enclosure for maintenance and inspection
		Periodic reinspection required to check for damage
		Repair of damaged enclosure necessary
		Fibers released in dry form during construction of enclosure
		Long-term costs could be higher than for removal

248

Method	Advantages	Disadvantages
Encapsulation	Reduces asbestos fiber release from material	Asbestos source remains and must be removed later
	Initial costs may be lower than for removal	If material is not in good condition, sealant may cause material to delaminate
	Does not require replacement of material	Periodic reinspection required to check for damage or deterioration
		Repair of damaged or deteriorating encapsulated surface required
		Encapsulated surface is difficult to remove and may require dry techniques for eventual removal
		Long-term costs may be higher than removal

REFERENCES

<u>Caution</u>

The atmosphere of each indoor environment is unique, with multiple biologic risks. Where and how we spend our time indoors determines the kind and degree of exposure that we have to such risks. The well-being of our immune systems and our biologic vitality lies within our physiologic and psychologic responses to the conditions of our varied environs.

Our vigilant awareness, choice, activities, and the buying and use of products, devices, and methods add to or subtract from our level of risk and wellness.

No endorsement or recommendation of the products, devices, and sources of information listed herein are made or implied. Within the author's experience, some benefits have occurred. But lack of standards for indoor air quality and air purification and unsubstantiated claims can confuse a potential buyer. Personal choice should be exercised with caution, preferably with the advice of an indoor air quality consultant, clinical ecologist, occupational health professional, or knowledgeable physician.

Very sensitive individuals who devote much effort and study to their individual problems often have the good fortune to find the "right" products, means of relief, and environment that make them comfortable and keep them well.

Books/Papers

Indoor Radon and Its Hazards by David Bodansky, Maurice Robkin, David Stadler. 156 pp. Available from:
University of Washington Press
P.O. Box 50096
Seattle, WA 98145

The Nontoxic Home by Debra Lynn Dadd. Los Angeles: Jeremy P. Tarcher, Inc., 1986. 213 pp.

Nontoxic & Natural by Debra Lynn Dadd. Los Angeles: Jeremy P. Tarcher, Inc., 1984, 1989. 289 pp.

Why Your Home May Endanger Your Health by Alfred V. Zamm. New York: Simon & Schuster, 1980. 218 pp.

The Healthy House by John Bower. New York: Carol Communications, 1989. 392 pp.

ASHRAE Handbook: 1977 Fundamentals by the American Society of Heating, Refrigerating and Air-Conditioning Engineers, Inc. New York: ASHRAE, 1977.

The Radon Industry Directory. Alexandria, VA: Radon Press, Inc. 540 pp.

Practical Radon Control for Homes. Available from:
Cutter Information Corp.
1100 Massachusetts Ave.
Arlington, MA 02174

Do You Want to Live Healthily?: A Survey of the Biology of House Construction by Karl E. Lotz. Remscheid, West Germany, 1982. 122 pp.

Biological Effects of Power Frequency Electric and Magnetic Fields - Background Paper by Indira Nair, M. Granger Morgan, H. Keith Florig. Washington, DC: Office of Technology Assessment, United States Congress, 1989. 103 pp.

Guidance for Controlling Asbestos-Containing Materials in Buildings: 1985 Edition by U.S. Environmental Protection Agency. Washington: U.S. Government Printing Office, 1987.

Cross Currents: The Promise of Electromedicine, The Perils of Electropollution by Robert O. Becker. Los Angeles: Jeremy P. Tarcher, Inc., 1990. 336 pp.

Heat Recovery Ventilation/Air-to-Air Heat Exchangers

ACS Hoval
935 N. Lively Blvd.
Wood Dale, IL 60191

The Air Changer Div.
Nortron Industries Ltd.
1140 Tristar Dr.
Mississauga, Ont., Canada
L5T 1H9

AirXChange, Inc.
30 Pond Park Rd.
Hingham, MA 02043

Astou Industries, Inc.
P.O. Box 220
St.-Leonard d'Aston
Quebec, Canada J0C 1M0

Berner International Corp.
P.O. Box 5205
New Castle, PA 16105

Blackhawk Industries, Inc.
607 Park St.
Regina, Sask., Canada S4N
5N1

BossAire
1321 Taylor St. N.E.
Minneapolis, MN 55413

Can Ray Inc.
255 Restigouche Rd.
Oromocto, N.B., Canada
E2V 2H1

Conservation Energy Systems
(Canadian) 3310 Millar Ave.
Saskatoon, Sask., Canada
S7K 7G9
(U.S.) Box 10416
Minneapolis, MN 55440

Des Champs Labs, Inc.
Box 440
East Hanover, NJ 07936

Enermatrix, Inc.
P.O. Box 446
Fargo, ND 58107

Ener-Quip
99 E. Kansas St.
Hackensack, NJ 07601

Engineering Development
Inc.
4750 Chromium Dr.
Colorado Springs, CO
80918

Environment Air Ltd.
P.O. Box 1128
Moncton, N.B.,
Canada E1C 8P6

Flakt, Inc.
Products Division
500 Shepherd St.
Winston-Salem, NC 27102

Future Energy Products Ltd.
184 Rocky Lake Rd.
Bedford, N.S.,
Canada B4A 2T6

Mountain Energy & Re-
sources, Inc.
15800 West Sixth Ave.
Golden, CO 80401

NewAire
7009 Raywood Rd.
Madison, WI 53713

Nutech Energy Systems, Inc.
97 Thames Rd. East
Box 640
Exeter, Ont.,
Canada N0M 1S0

Nutone Inc. Scovill
Madison and Red Bank Rds.
Cincinnati, OH 45227

P.M. Wright Ltd.
1300 Jules-Poitras
Montreal, Que.,
Canada H4N 1X8

Q-Dot Corp.
701 N. First St.
Garland, TX 75040

Standex Energy Systems
P.O. Box 1168
Detroit Lakes, MN 56501

Star Heat Exchanger Corp.
B-109 1772 Broadway St.
Fort Coquitiam, B.C.,
Canada V3C 2M8

Xetex, Inc.
3530 E. 28th St.
Minneapolis, MN 55406

Air Cleaning Equipment

Penox Technologies, Inc.
One Penox Plaza
Pittson, PA 18640-0785
(HEPA, charcoal) "Air One"

Bionaire Corporation
565A Commerce St.
Franklin Lakes, NJ 07417
(electret, neg ion) "Bionaire
500", "BT 1500" (electro-
static, charcoal)

AllerMed Corporation
31 Steel Rd.
Wylie, TX 75098
(HEPA, charcoal, neg ion)
"Airstar"

Teledyne Water Pik
1730 E. Prospect St.
Fort Collins, CO 80525
(charcoal, catalytic, HEPA)
"Instapure"

Mason Engineering Corp.
242 Devon Ave.
Bensonville, IL 60106
(charcoal, HEPA) "Cloud 9"

Newtron Products Company
3874 Viginia Avenue
P.O. Box 27175
Cincinnati, OH 45227-0175
(static electric)

Honeywell, Inc.
1985 Douglas Drive North
Golden Valley, MN 55422-
3992
(charcoal, electrostatic)

LakeAir International, Inc.
P.O. Box 4150
Racine, WI 53404
(charcoal, electrostatic)

Trion, Inc.
P.O. Box 760
Sanford, NC 27331
(charcoal, electrostatic)
"MAX 4"

United Air Specialists, Inc.
4440 Creek Rd.
Cincinnati, OH 45242
(charcoal, electrostatic, neg
ion) "SMOKEETER"

Metal-Fab Inc.
P.O. Box 1138
Wichita, KS 67201
(charcoal, HEPA) "Micro Air"

PuriDyne
3216B Wellington Court
Raleigh, NC 27615
(biogenic air purification)

Vita-Mix Corporation
8615 Usher Rd.
Cleveland, OH 44138
(vacuum/air cleaner)
"Vita-Vac"

Oreck Corporation
100 Plantation Road
New Orleans, LA 70123
(hypo-allergenic vacuum
cleaner) "Celoc"

Sande Corporation
P.O. Box 415
Mason, OH 45040
(molecular adsorber)
"Miss Molley"

G & W Supply
4100 W. 38th Avenue
Denver, CO 80212
(molecular adsorber)
"Odor-Fresh"

Mia Rose Products, Inc.
1374 Logan Ave. #C
Costa Mesa, CA 92626
(ionized air mist)
"Air Therapy"

Enviracaire Corporation
747 Bowman Avenue
Hagerstown, MD 27140
(charcoal prefilter, HEPA)
"Enviracaire"

Negative Ion Equipment

Ion Systems, Inc.
2546 Tenth St.
Berkeley, CA 94710
"Pulsair" "AirEase"

American Environmental Systems, Inc.
4699 Nautilus Court South
Boulder, CO 80301
(ionization/Schumann positive field resonance)

Radon Mitigation Products

Safe-Aire, Inc.
162 E. Chestnut St.
Canton, IL 61520
(mail order vendor)

Akzo Industrial Systems Co.
One North Pack Square
P.O. Box 7249
Asheville, NC 28802
"Enkavent" (radon control matting)

Ion Systems, Inc.
2546 Tenth St.
Berkeley, CA 94710
(neg ion) "No-Rad"

Energy Saver Imports, Inc.
2150 W. 6th Ave., Unit E
Broomfield, CO 80020
"Foil Ray" (radon barrier and insulation)

Natural Finishes, Paints, Waxes, Etc.

LIVOS PlantChemistry
614 Agua Fria St.
Santa Fe, NM 87501
AURO

SINAN CO. (Importer)
P.O. Box 181
Suisan City, CA 94585
(produced in W. Germany and Austria)

Clean Rooms

American Environmental Systems, Inc.
4699 Nautilus Court South
Boulder, CO 80301
(electrophoresis effect clean rooms, radon mitigation)

Detection and Monitoring Equipment

Bacharach Inc.
625 Alpha Dr.
Pittsburgh, PA 15238
(carbon monoxide detectors)
"Monoxor Indicator" "Monoxor Detector"

Quantum Group
11211 Sorrento Valley Rd.
San Diego, CA 92121
(carbon monoxide alarm)
"CO-Star 9A-i"

Threshold Technical Products
Dept. 707
11325 Reed Hartman Highway
Cincinnati, OH 45241
(radon monitor) "Survivor 2"

Sun Nuclear Corporation
415-C Pineda Court
Melbourne, FL 32940-7597
(radon monitors) "At Ease"

Thomson & Nielsen Electronics Ltd.
4019 Carling Ave.
Kanata, Ontario
Canada K2K 2A3
(radon metering) "Radon Sniffer"

Bio-Physics Mersmann, Inc.
29 Harvard Rd.
Belmont, MA 02178
(electromagnetic field detection equipment)

"E/M Fieldmeter Kombi-Test" measures 60-cycle AC electromagnetic fields (electric field measurement range 0 - 100 V/m, magnetic field 0 - 1,000 nanoTeslas with second coil)

"Geo-Magnetometer BPM 2001" measures the DC electromagnetic fields of the earth (available with a data logger and stylus recorder for computer graphics)

Swimming and Hot Spa Pool Water Purification Equipment

Diamond Shamrock
Electrolytic Systems Division
470 Center St.
Chardon, OH 44024
(electrolytic chlorination)
"Lectronator Chlorinator"

Air Quality Sensor

Johnson Controls, Inc.
Systems and Services Division
P.O. Box 423
Milwaukee, WI 53201-0423

An air quality sensor has been developed that can detect numerous major contaminants present in indoor air. In response to the sensor, more or less outdoor intake air can be introduced for specific ventilation of indoor spaces by a mechanical air distribution system. The sensors can also determine the degree of pollution present in outdoor air.

The sensor could have a revolutionary effect upon the design of HVAC systems. It is of special note as a means to greatly improve indoor air quality and to significantly lessen the possibility of "sick building syndrome."

Electron Generator

Air Physics Corporation
1 Northfield Plaza
Northfield, IL 60093

Computer Radiation Protection

Natural Energy Works
P.O. Box 1395
El Cerrito, CA 94530
(VDT screen shield)
"EYEGUARD-XP"

Radiation and Environmental Surveys

The Planetary Association for Clean Energy, Inc.
100 Bronson Avenue / 1001
OTTAWA, Ontario K1R 6G8 CANADA

A interdisciplinary network of scientists offers environmental and occupational health surveys that focus on assessment of electromagnetic fields at a particular location.

Solar Technologic and Biomass Fuels Research

Solar Energy Research Institute
1617 Cole Boulevard
Golden, CO 80401

GLOSSARY

adsorption - removal of gaseous contaminants from the air by their adherence on the surface of a material

aerosols - fine solid or liquid particles in a gaseous suspension in the air that settle very slowly under the force of gravity

air exchange rate - the number of times the volume of air in a space is exchanged with outdoor air in a specified amount of time, usually expressed in air changes per hour (ACH)

air exhaust - removal of air from a space through natural or forced (mechanical) means

air tempering - heating or cooling incoming outside air to condition it for natural or mechanical ventilation

aldehydes - a class of highly reactive organic compounds containing the chemical group CHO and having strong odors

allergen - a substance that induces allergy; aero-allergens are particulates of natural or synthetic origin capable of producing an allergic reaction when present in the atmosphere

alpha particle - a positively charged particle emitted from the decay of a radioactive element

alpha radiation - a form of low-level, ionizing radiation

beta particle - charged particle (electron or positron) emitted in certain radioactive transformations

263

carbon monoxide (CO) - colorless, odorless, toxic gas formed as a byproduct of incomplete combustion

combustion appliance - any fuel-burning (oil, gas, coal, kerosene, or wood) device used as a range, furnace, water heater, or clothes dryer

concentration - the quantity of one constituent dispersed in a defined amount of another; parts per million, for example

Curie (Ci) - a unit of radioactivity equal to 3.7×10^{10} disintegrations per second

diffusion - spontaneous movement of particles of liquids, gases, or solids in a dissolved substance from a region of higher to one of lower concentration

dispersion - movement of contaminants throughout the air by diffusion and mixing

dust - an air suspension of particles of any solid material, usually less than 100 microns in size

emission rate - amount of contaminant released into the air by a source in a specified amount of time

filter medium - a substance used as a filter

formaldehyde (HCHO) - colorless air contaminant outgassed from many materials, used in the manufacture of resins and dyes, and as a preservative and disinfectant

gamma radiation - penetrating electromagnetic radiation emitted from the decay of some radioactive elements

half-life - the time required for half of the atoms of a radioactive substance to become disintegrated

HEPA - high efficiency particulate air (filter)

Hertz (Hz) - a unit of frequency equal to one cycle per second

inductive ventilation - natural ventilation enhanced and induced through a rising air column generated by temperature differentials

infiltration - the uncontrolled movement of outdoor air into the interior of a building through cracks around doors and windows or in walls, roofs, and floors

intake air - see "ventilation air"

ion - an electrically charged atom or group of atoms caused by gain or loss of one or more electrons

mechanical ventilation - forced movement of air by fans into and out of a building

micron - unit of length equal to one-millionth of a meter, also known as micrometer

natural ventilation - unaided movement of air into and out of an enclosed space through intentionally provided openings

negative ionization - introduction of negative ions into a space, often for air-cleaning purposes

outgassing (offgassing) - emission of gases and/or respirable particles during the aging and degradation of a material; usually refers to emission of toxic contaminants from unstable synthetic materials, maintenance products, and finishes used in indoor environments

particulates - matter in which solid or liquid substances exist in the form of aggregated molecules; airborne particulates typically range in size from 0.01 to 20 microns

picocurie - one-trillionth (10^{-12}) part of a Curie

positive field (positive resonance) - a positively charged electrostatic field, used in conjunction with negative ionization to collect and ground out airborne particles

prefilter - initial filter on an air-cleaning machine that removes large particles

radon (Radon-222) - an inert, radioactive gas formed by the disintegration of radium in soils and rock formations

radon "daughters" (radon progeny) - radon gas decay products formed by disintegration of radon nuclei; several of these are alpha radiation emitters

respirable particles - particles that penetrate to the lungs when inhaled; upper size limit is approximately 5 microns

return air - air returned from conditioned, heated, or refrigerated spaces

sidestream smoke (secondhand smoke, passive smoking) - tobacco smoke that goes directly into the air from the burning end of a cigar, cigarette, or pipe; not inhaled by the smoker

suspended particles - extremely small particles that remain suspended in the air and settle out only slowly under the force of gravity; upper size limit is approximately 100 microns

total suspended particles - quantifies the weight of particulate matter suspended in a unit volume of air

toxic - referring to the capability of a substance to produce a harmful health effect after physical contact, ingestion, or inhalation

ventilation - the process of supplying and removing air by natural and/or mechanical means to and from any space

ventilation air - outside air that is intentionally caused to enter an interior space

7572 4091